A HISTORY OF THE ROYAL MARSDEN HOSPITAL

A HISTORY OF THE ROYAL MARSDEN HOSPITAL

Eve Wiltshaw
OBE MD FRCP FRCOG
Director of Clinical Services and Consultant Physician
The Royal Marsden Hospital

ALTMAN

Published by Altman Publishing, 65 Lake View, Edgware, Middlesex, HA8 7SA

First edition 1998

© 1998 Eve Wiltshaw

Typeset in 12/15 Garamond by Saxon Graphics Ltd, Derby

Printed in Great Britain by TJ International Ltd, Padstow, Cornwall

ISBN 1 86036 009 2

All rights reserved. No part of this publication may be reproduced, stored in a retrieval system or transmitted in any form or by any means, electronic, mechanical, photocopying, recording or otherwise, without the prior written permission of the publishers. Applications for permission should be addressed to the publisher at the London address printed on this page.

The publisher makes no representation, express or implied, with regard to the accuracy of the information contained in this book and cannot accept any legal responsibility or liability for any errors or omissions that may be made.

A catalogue record for this book is available from the British Library

∞ Printed on acid-free text paper, manufactured in accordance with ANSI/NISO Z39.48-1992 (Permanence of Paper)

CONTENTS

FOREWORD

The story of the Royal Marsden Hospital, so well outlined by Dr. Wiltshaw, herself an extremely distinguished oncologist, is a fascinating one. The Hospital was founded in 1851 and this history takes the story up to 1995, when it became a National Health Service Trust.

Dr. William Marsden, the founder, was a remarkable man who built two free hospitals – the Royal Free and the Royal Marsden. He had a large surgical practice and was a well-loved doctor. Three chapters chronicle the expansion of staff, activities and buildings, together with the constant battles for survival in the face of continuous hostility from the general medical establishment and the Ministry. The important part played in our survival by good governance and, above all by the support of the public, is given in a special chapter. Whether at Chelsea or Sutton, the Hospital has established itself with a reputation that spreads far beyond its normal parish.

Various chapters cover the progress of surgery, physics and radiotherapy and medicine, together with specialist cancer nursing. There is a section devoted to the information technology, which was developed in-house in the 1970s. Colourful and innovative individuals are picked out for special mention and the occasional minor scandals also figure.

There is a description of the origin of the Institute of Cancer Research, which was born in the Hospital in 1907 and later became a separate entity with the coming of the National Health Service.

The two organizations now function as one Institution although there is no formal or legal affiliation. Each is dependent on the other. The results in research and patient care speak for themselves, supplemented as they are by the dedicated work of all our staff, scientists, consultants and nurses.

It is a fascinating story, well told and records the history and evolution of the Hospital and Institute, which are playing an increasingly large part in the perennial battle against this dreadful disease.

Lord Hussey of North Bradley

PREFACE

The story of an institution, especially one whose sole purpose is the care of sick and vulnerable people, is more about the staff and their attitudes and actions than about bricks and mortar. This history concentrates on the major players in the 150 years of the life of the Royal Marsden Hospital and the author apologizes to all those – both living and dead – who have not been mentioned by name, and the many who will feel aggrieved that their contributions have not been singled out. The story is far from complete in this short volume and much more could have been added if written documentation had been available. Perhaps others will be encouraged to fill in the gaps some time in the future.

The Hospital was founded to care for patients suffering from a particular pathological problem – cancer – and there has always been controversy about its value in comparison with other institutions, in particular the London teaching hospitals, to further the cause of best research, treatment and care. I believe that even this incomplete history will show that up to now its value has been self-evident. In the future its relevance will depend on a continuing entrepreneurial spirit and a willingness to try new approaches, while always retaining its most enduring characteristic, the primacy of the patient in all its thinking and planning.

So many people have helped in this endeavour that it is probably invidious to name only a few, but I must mention those who managed to supply written information, which has been invaluable. In this regard my thanks go to Len Lamerton and David Galton, both of whom loaned me copies of the scripts of historical talks they had given. My thanks, too, to Clive Harmer who supplied documents about the radiotherapy department. My especial thanks go to Jo Milan, who helped in writing the chapter on Information Technology, and to Brian Lake who did likewise for the chapter on Nursing and Nurse Training. I acknowledge the help of many others who were willing to talk to me about their experiences at the hospital – all were of great value. Lastly, I want to thank the photographic departments at both Sutton and London for their time and effort in producing the illustrations, and Penny Cousins, secretary to the chief executive, who took the trouble to help me find the relevant minutes, annual reports and other documents.

Chapter 1

DR WILLIAM MARSDEN

William Marsden, the founder of the Royal Marsden and the Royal Free Hospitals in London, was born in Sheffield in September 1796. He was the eldest of eight children and while his father seems to have been a stern disciplinarian his mother was said to be kind and sweet natured. Nevertheless William seems to have had a reasonably happy childhood in a family with no particular economic problems. But William enjoyed his holidays at his grandfather's farm most, where he took pleasure in caring for the animals and tasting the joys of the countryside. His grandfather, David Marsden, was sympathetic to William's desire to learn and later to his ambition to become a surgeon, an aspiration his father thought ridiculous.

When William left school he managed to persuade his father to apprentice him to a Mr Hodgkinson, a local wholesale druggist, where he learned quickly and his services were greatly appreciated. Indeed, when he was only 19 years old he was offered a partnership. He turned it down, insisting that he must go to London and become a surgeon. William quarrelled with his father over this decision, and he left home without any monetary support and apparently without the consent of his parents. His grandfather gave him about six guineas to help him on his way and, no doubt, some good advice.

William took the stagecoach from York to London, and on the journey befriended a girl of 12 called Elizabeth Ann Bishop who was travelling alone. She had recently lost her mother, and her father was sending her to Chelsea to be cared for by an aunt. William Marsden, even at that young age, showed how he cared for the weak and defenceless, and the little girl took to him immediately. However, when they reached London she left before he could discover where she was staying. Marsden must have had a very attractive personality, for he made friends wherever he went. He was also blessed with good luck, for the very night he arrived in London he found an apothecary's shop. Its familiarity encouraged him to enter. The owner invited him to tea and after William had shown his credentials and told his story he was offered lodgings and employment. He stayed only a short time, for he was determined to become apprenticed to a surgeon and to start his training. His new friend the apothecary introduced him to Mr Dale, a local surgeon. Mr Dale was getting on in years and already had one assistant, but William impressed him and he offered him a post as a qualified druggist and assistant in spite of the fact that William had no money to buy his apprenticeship.

As a possible rival to Mr Dale's nephew Edmund, William's tact was now all-important and he managed to keep Edmund's friendship despite the fact that Edmund was not exactly a hard worker, while William was fanatical in this regard. Having satisfactorily arranged his own affairs William set about trying to find his young girl friend. He knew only that she lived in Chelsea, so he went to a different church in the area every Sunday, knowing she would be attending one of them. He found her at St. Lukes. He introduced himself to her aunt, Mrs Hamilton, and was permitted to take her niece out and about and to visit them at home. Thus their friendship continued.

It was essential for William's training for him to gain experience in human dissection so he joined the Anatomical School of Joshua Brookes in Blenheim Street. There were many of these private schools, as well as teaching hospitals, all competing for bodies for dissection, and soon the Royal College of Surgeons insisted that all anatomical training must be done in the teaching hospitals, freezing out the private schools. Marsden moved to St. Bartholomew's Hospital for further

Figure 1.1 Young Dr William Marsden

instruction under John Abernathy, who was a good teacher and an excellent surgeon, though not a wonderful anatomist. Nevertheless Marsden qualified as a Member of the Royal College of Surgeons in 1827. When Mrs Hamilton discovered that he was dissecting bodies she forbade him any further contact with Betsy Ann, and sent her niece away to a seminary for young ladies for the next three years. But they kept in contact by mail and when she returned, still aged only 16, they asked her father's permission to marry. He still lived in Yorkshire and made no objection, so the youngsters married on 29 January 1820, when William was 23.

Figure 1.2 Betsy Ann, William Marsden's first wife

By this time William was earning a reasonable amount from his practice with Mr Dale and Edmund, but when Mr Dale died suddenly the practice was left to the two young men as partners. They attempted to make the partnership work but it was not long before Marsden struck out on his own, taking most of the patients with him and setting up his surgery at 2, Thavies Inn.

The Marsdens had their first child late in 1820 but he died in the first few weeks of life. The second boy, born two years later, died in his second year during an epidemic of childhood infection, to the great distress of his parents. It was not until 1827 that they had a third child – a healthy daughter. It was in that same year that the doctor realized the full iniquity of the hospital admission system of the time. He found an 18-year-old prostitute desperately ill on the steps of a church as he walked home in the snow one evening, and took pity on her. He took her by cab to St. Bartholomew's but she was not admitted because he was not a governor, so could not give a letter of introduction. He tried St. Thomas's and Guys' hospitals, with the same result. In the end he took the girl to lodgings near his home and looked after her there until she died. Marsden must have known that this kind of problem occurred every day in London but the personal encounter brought it home to him and, it is said, was a turning point in his career. He knew he was not rich enough to help on his own but he had wealthy patients and friends, and he determined to found a new hospital where the only entry requirements would be the presence of disease and the fact of poverty. Remarkably, within 8 weeks he had gathered 27 businessmen from the City to a meeting to discuss the project. There was much opposition but some who sympathized, including Alderman James Harmer, who was to be a staunch friend over many years. On 14 February 1828 the committee met and the first free hospital was established in a rented house.

In the first 10 months 926 patients were seen. Despite many ups and downs, together with endless headaches over funding, the Free Hospital went from strength to strength and opened its doors to admit patients when the cholera epidemic struck in 1832. Other hospitals did not admit cholera sufferers and when the epidemic was over Marsden wanted to continue admissions for other illnesses. He managed to keep just 6 beds open for 'serious illnesses' despite continuing financial difficulties at times amounting to near bankruptcy.

Other troubles at the hospital included the use of quack medicines by some doctors against Marsden's instructions – he felt this was serious exploitation of the sick. This did not make him popular with some doctors, among them Mr Astley Cooper and his son, powerful people in the profession at the time.

In June 1837 the young Queen Victoria came to the throne and in the same year she agreed to be patron and granted the

Royal title to the Free Hospital. This was a great boost to the hospital subscriptions and to its reputation with the public.

Events seemed to favour William at this time, for he obtained a doctorate of medicine in 1838. His daughter Elizabeth was a joy to him, and his last child Alexander was healthy. However, 1840 was a disaster. Elizabeth died of scarlet fever while away in France and his wife's health began to fail. It is strange but true that doctors often ignore signs of serious illness in their own families – William did not seem to realize that his wife was fatally afflicted. He continued to be overloaded with concerns about the viability of the Royal Free Hospital and his large practice. Always having to beg for more funds from the rich is an exhausting business and it kept him away from home a lot. But his concern for others was recognized when the Cordwainers Company in the City of London gave him a testimonial service of silver plate which was presented by the Duke of Cambridge in 1842 to commemorate the foundation of the Free Hospital.

By 1845 it was clear that William's wife was dying and he began to rely more heavily on a family friend, Elizabeth Abbot, to run his household. Betsy Ann died in 1846 of an internal cancer – perhaps of the cervix. Her last months were full of pain for which she took increasing doses of laudanum. Shortly after her death Marsden married Elizabeth Abbot and they moved into a new home in Lincoln's Inn Fields. It was, perhaps, the death and preceding misery of his first wife's illness which was the driving force for William Marsden to found a second hospital for cancer sufferers. He was not deterred by all the trials and tribulations he had endured during the early years of the Royal Free Hospital, or by its continuing debts and the hostility of the medical profession.

In 1851 he embarked on this new venture with all his usual determination. One might say that he was a glutton for punishment. On 10 February he held a meeting at his home with 12 friends. He is quoted as saying, 'Now gentlemen, I want to found a hospital for the treatment of cancer, and the study of

Figure 1.3 Dr Marsden in later life with a drawing of the Royal Free Hospital

the disease, for at the present time we know absolutely nothing about it.' Only three months later the Cancer Hospital opened its doors. William was the senior surgeon and he supported and served the Hospital until his death, often giving or lending money but always striving to do more for the cancer patients and looking for answers to the unending grim questions posed by the disease.

Marsden was 55 when the second hospital opened to patients in 1851. He was dividing his time between supporting two hospitals and a large private practice. There must have been little time for leisure and home life. Nevertheless he now suggested that it was time for a medical school to be started at the Royal Free Hospital and plans were made for a new building there. The school was opened in 1877 for female medical students, the first in England to do so.

Marsden must have been gratified when his son became a surgeon and joined him in his work at both his hospitals. Marsden died after a short illness on 16 January 1867, aged 71. He was never honoured by the sovereign, although five years earlier a deputation had approached the Secretary of State to ask that his services be recognized. Today he would undoubtedly have received a knighthood at least.

The continued and flourishing existence of his two hospitals after more than 150 years would probably be his greatest reward, together with advances in the treatment of disease and the reduction of poverty. His obituary in the *Lancet* of 26 January 1867 states, 'Besides the foresight which enabled him to guage the wants of the age, his singular and intuitive knowledge of character enabled him so to adapt his deportment to the individual he wished to influence, that few came in contact with him who did not feel that he had a persuasive power not easily resisted; and thus he enjoyed for many years a very large circle of friends who were ever ready to help him in all his public undertakings.' Later it points out, 'to him alone belongs the credit of introducing the free system of admission now adopted by almost all our leading medical charities.'

Chapter 2

THE EARLY YEARS (1851–1900)

The Free Cancer Hospital, conceived by William Marsden and 12 of his friends and supporters, may have been started because Marsden had seen many patients suffering from cancer, and had watched his first wife and love, Betsy Ann, dying from uterine or cervical cancer after a long period of pain and distress.

The Hospital at first consisted only of a dispensary at 1 Cannon Row, Westminster and from the start Dr Marsden insisted on keeping faithful statistics of who came and which sites of the body were affected. He also wanted to try to look for causes of the disease, to classify the types of tumour and to try out new (but not quack) therapies.

The figures were reported in the Annual Reports and by 1853, 654 patients had been seen of whom 80% were women. At this time, however, very little could be done to help patients apart from palliative care, while some of the commonly practised remedies caused dreadful suffering. Among these were the use of caustics, the occasional surgical excision without the benefit of anaesthetic or antisepsis and compression of tumour. From its inception the Hospital was committed to investigate the cancerous process, its causes, early diagnosis and treatment. With a concentration of cases in one establishment the Hospital was able to state as early as 1854 that in the opinion of its surgeons 'the disease is a constitutional disease lying dormant, and springing forth when thus excited to action, we have every reason to believe, notwithstanding the facts shown, that only one in six have the evidence of a hereditary predisposition within them. The strong ground for asserting it to be a constitutional, and not a local disease, is the return of the disease in the same or other parts of the body after operation.'

Furthermore the surgeons, mainly, one suspects, under the influence of William Marsden, believed in treating the whole person, not just the cancerous part. The surgical report of 1854 continues, '84 cases that have been operated on have come before us, and the average lapse of time before the disease reappeared was a year and a half. Although this is not an argument against operation in selected cases, and we have ourselves been enabled to prolong life in comparative comfort by operations in the most advanced cases, it nevertheless urges the combination of constitutional remedies, and to the employment of these in the various stages of the disease we have directed our special attention, as our case books will show.'

The Hospital was not averse to looking at other institutions to see if they could improve on their care of cancer patients and the Board sent William Marsden to Europe to investigate. He visited France and Belgium in 1856 and intended to go to Germany and Austria especially to discuss the rapidly growing subject of pathology. There had been a cancer hospital in France, probably the first in the world, founded by Jean Godinot in 1740. But *'La Lutte Contre Cancer de Rheims'* closed only a few years later so the Cancer Hospital in London was unique. However there were cancer specialists, and Marsden seems to have been particularly impressed by the French surgeon M Velpeau of the 'Hôpital de la Charité' who had written a treatise on *'Diseases of the breast and the mammary region, their nature and treatment'*. William Marsden translated this treatise for the benefit of other hospital practitioners. He emphasized his disagreement with the European doctors about the importance of 'constitutional' treatment, presumably diet and drugs, and he ascribed lack of knowledge about these measures to the isolation of physicians from surgeons, which he thought should not occur in cancer management.

For the first 10 years of the Cancer Hospital's existence it was most concerned with raising sufficient funds to cover the care of rising numbers of patients coming to its doors, then with improving the facilities available, in particular patient accommodation. By 1853 the total income amounted to £3,196 19s 1d, all coming from annual subscriptions or donations. In that year the list of donors took up eight pages of typescript – three years later a similar list covered 21 pages, while public support continued to grow. This was despite the hostility of the medical profession generally and even of the monarch. Queen Victoria had been asked to support the foundation of the Hospital but had declined, presumably on advice, in rather harsh terms. She wrote 'Her Majesty must decline contributing to a hospital for the exclusive treatment of one disorder, the sufferers under which malady are not excluded from general hospitals.' Fortunately she later changed her mind and gave a generous donation.

The generosity of friends of the Hospital and of the general public was such that 30 years after its foundation the funds could support out-patient care and in-patient management of 80 beds, as well as the formation of a capital investment portfolio. As far as capital required for buildings was concerned the Board relied heavily on several large contributors, some of whom were Board members. The growth in patient numbers meant that between 1851 and 1862 when the hospital building in Fulham Road was opened, various moves were made. After opening the dispensary at Cannon Row it soon became apparent that some patients had to be admitted especially for operations. In November 1852 a house in Hollywood Road, west London was leased at a rental of £63 per annum to house six in-patient beds. In 1854 the dispensary moved from Cannon Row to 5 Waterloo Place, Pall Mall, where an administrative office was set up. However, a year later it moved again from Pall Mall to 167 Piccadilly.

Figure 2.1 Baroness Burdett-Coutts

In 1855 the board obtained the patronage of Baroness Burdett-Coutts, whose loan of £3,000 made possible the purchase of the Fulham Road site of about an acre at a cost of £4,500. Matters then proceeded architect, David Mocatta gave his services free and building commenced on the basis of the lowest submitted tender. These varied from £5,240 to £5,995. The foundation stone was laid by Baroness Coutts at a ceremony on 30 May 1859. The Bishop of London presided as the band of the Coldstream Guards provided musical entertainment to a large gathering in the hospital grounds. On that day the bells of nearby St. Luke's Church were rung in celebration and a foundation dinner was held at the Thatched House Tavern in St. James' Street.

The design of the Hospital allowed for expansion by adding wings to the original front block. The long-term plan was for a 300-bed establishment in a square format with a central garden, but the original design was never to be completed. Some activity started on the new building in 1861 but the project was not completed until the following year when just 30 of a possible 80 beds were available for use in six wards. The Board had insufficient income to support more. The staffing consisted of three honorary surgeons, William Marsden and his son Alexander and a Mr Weedon Cooke, who had joined at the Hospital's inception. Alexander had joined after his return from military service in Scutari during the Crimean war. A Matron was appointed, a Miss Scrivener, as well as a resident house surgeon, while Robert Knox was the anatomist and a Mr Draper was resident dispenser.

Robert Knox was the son of a mathematician and a qualified MD (Edinburgh University, 1814). He served with the army at Waterloo and later went to South Africa. He joined a famous school of anatomy, the Barclay School, and soon became a partner. He was an excellent anatomist and lecturer who often had 400 or more students. He needed bodies for these young men to dissect, and like all anatomy schools at that time he paid up to £25 for each one. The authorities' fail-

Figure 2.2 The final hospital as planned by the architect David Moccatta but never completed

Figure 2.3 The Cancer Hospital building opened in 1862

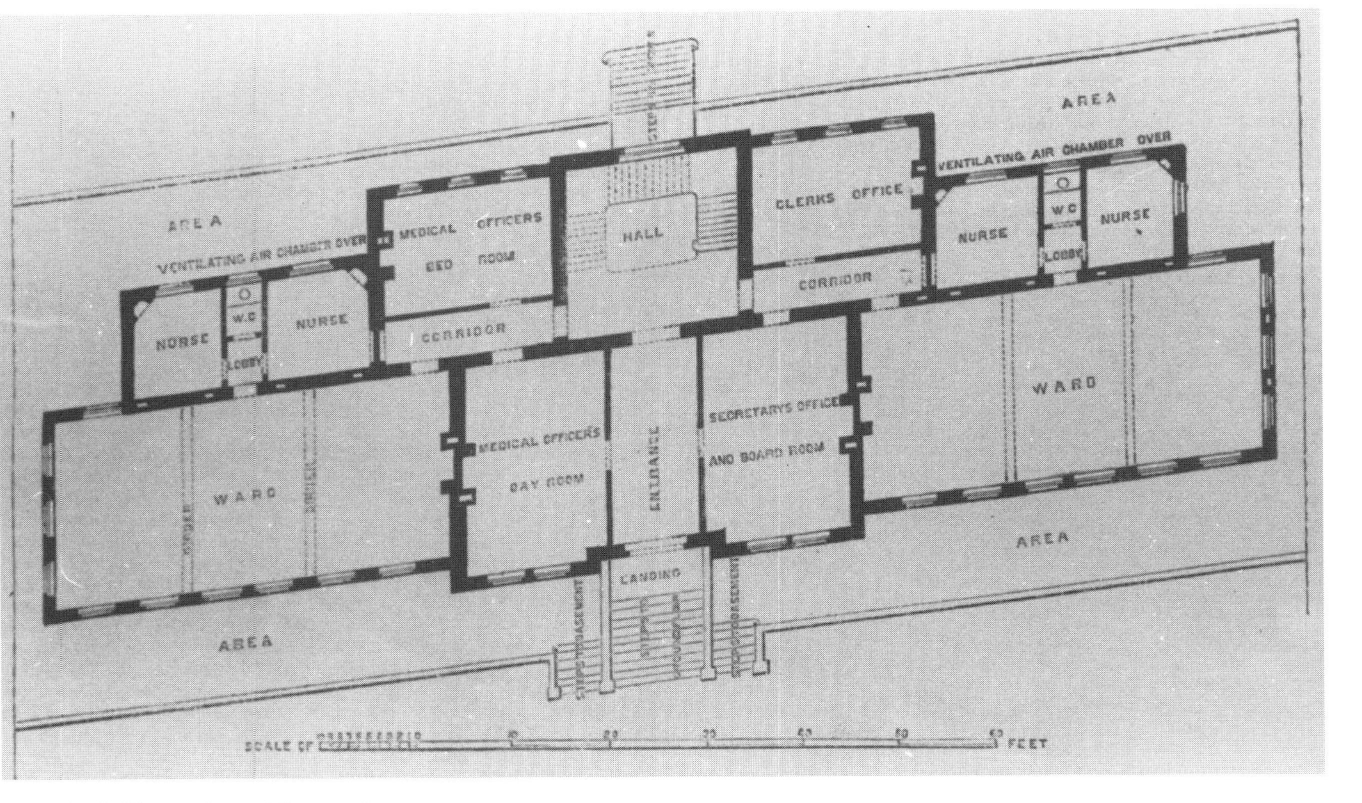

Figure 2.4 The original floor plan

ure to recognize the need of medical students to have corpses for dissection led to a whole unsavoury industry of selling bodies, often obtained by grave robbing. The men involved in the trade became known as the resurrectionists. The practice was established many years before Knox began his classes. However in 1827 Hare and Burke went further, and started to murder people in order to sell their bodies. They were caught and convicted only after they had killed 15 people and some of the bodies had been purchased by the Barclay School. The school and Knox denied all knowledge of the murders but Knox, although never charged with any illegality, was hounded and lost his reputation entirely. The school closed and eventually Knox came to London after he had failed to gain entry to academic life in Glasgow. He was never accepted by the universities and seems to have lived by his writing, lecturing and some medical practice. He wrote bitterly about the machinations of medical and academic politics, 'as to elevation to real power, why, mediocrity is your only chance; it secures you entrance into good society, a *fauteuil* at the council table of all the Royal Societies'. Dr Knox came late in life to the Cancer Hospital and probably added little to the advancement of cancer knowledge, but he did start a museum of interesting pathological specimens, drawings and models of diseased organs. Unfortunately none are extant.

From the outset there had been rules for the medical staff. Among these were the annual reviews of all appointments and all senior medical staff had to have either the FRCP, LRCP, in the case of physicians, and MRCS for surgeons.

By 1862 the Board reported that 4804 patients had been seen between 1851 and 1862, of whom 154 were said to 'have been discharged cured' with or without operation. In fact only a few had been operated on in the Hospital, although 392 of the more than 4000 patients were submitted to surgery elsewhere. The report also shows that 857 patients were referred although they did not have cancer.

Figure 2.5 Group photograph taken in the Hospital garden between 1862 and 1866: William Marsden and his son are on the extreme right

William Marsden died in January 1867 and the measure of his loss was recorded by the Board in the following terms:

> 'In presenting their 16th annual report to the friends and subscribers of the Cancer Hospital the committee advert with profound regret the lamented decease of the late Dr Marsden to whose benevolent sagacity and zeal this charity owes its origin. So long as this gentleman's failing health permitted him to prescribe for the numerous patients afflicted with this terrible malady his great skill, experience and humanity were cheerfully devoted to their service. Dr Marsden rests from his labours but his works do follow him in the successful establishment through the liberal co-operation of his friends and the public of the two great medical charities: The Cancer Hospital at Brompton and The Royal Free Hospital at Grey's Inn Lane, with both of which his name will be henceforth gratefully associated in the great annals of philanthropy.'

William's son took over as senior surgeon but while he seems to have been as caring as his father he did not have the flair or drive for constant improvement. His surgeon's reports are henceforth shorter, duller and more repetitive.

By 1870 the Hospital had attracted much interest abroad. Visitors came from many countries including Russia, Germany and America. The Empress of Russia planned to start a similar hospital in St Petersburg but it was not until 1886 that another cancer institute (The Beatson Institute) was founded – in Glasgow.

In the 1860s the staff was increased to include a 'chloroformist' about 20 years after the discovery in the USA of nitrous oxide as an anaesthetic (1844). Ether was first used in 1849 and in 1858 James Simpson introduced chloroform, which became the favoured anaesthetic agent in this country. The appointment of a chloroformist was only necessary when there were sufficient beds available to allow regular surgical procedures, that is after 1862. By 1875 the surgeons had oper-

Figure 2.6 Wilson ward before 1895, when electric light was introduced

ated on 449 patients. Surgery became considerably safer after the introduction of an antisepsis policy nine years after Lister introduced carbolic into surgical practice in 1865.

In the 1880s a new wing containing more wards was built. Costs for this amounted to £24,359 but it enabled all the office accommodation and out-patient services to be transferred from the Piccadilly site. Cancer cases were now classified by histological appearance and a fully trained histopathologist was badly needed to replace surgeons who had hitherto been doing their own microscopy. The post carried a grand salary of £60 per annum and a Mr Stoneham FRCS, was appointed. The hospital also started a course of lectures on cancer during January to March each year, run by Dr Snow. Three main topics were discussed: the theory and general pathology of cancer; the recurrence of cancer and its prevention; and palliative treatment. Surgery continued to dominate as the treatment of choice and by the end of the century there were six surgeons, two anaesthetists, two house surgeons and two pathologists on the staff.

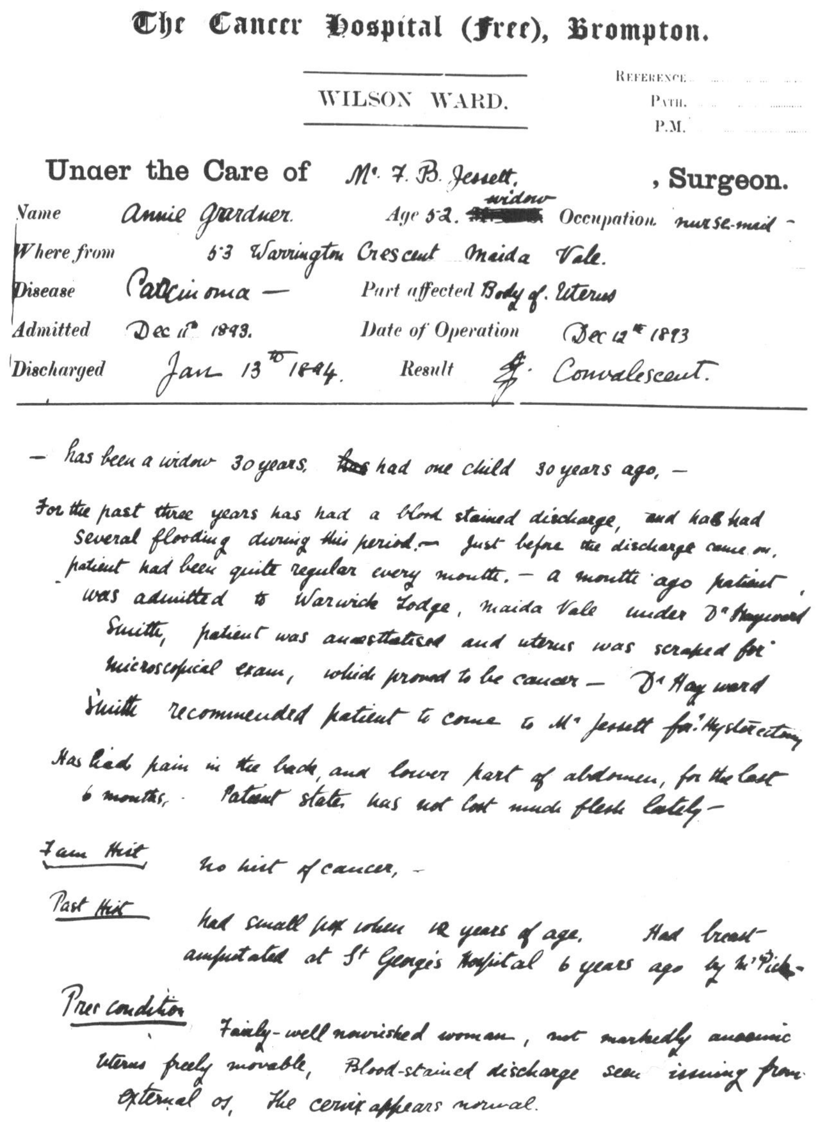

The Cancer Hospital (Free), Brompton.

WILSON WARD.

REFERENCE
PATH.
P.M.

Under the Care of Mr. F. B. Jessett, **Surgeon.**

Name Annie Gardner. Age 52. widow Occupation nurse-maid –
Where from 53 Warrington Crescent Maida Vale.
Disease Carcinoma – Part affected Body of Uterus
Admitted Dec 11th 1893. Date of Operation Dec 12th 1893
Discharged Jan 13th 1894. Result Convalescent.

– has been a widow 30 years, has had one child 30 years ago, –

For the past three years has had a blood stained discharge, and has had several flooding during this period. – Just before the discharge came on, patient had been quite regular every month. – a month ago patient was admitted to Warwick Lodge, Maida Vale under Dr Hayward Smith, patient was anaesthetised and uterus was scraped for microscopical exam, which proved to be cancer – Dr Hayward Smith recommended patient to come to Mr Jessett for Hysterectomy

Has had pain in the back, and lower part of abdomen, for the last 6 months. Patient states has not lost much flesh lately –

Fam Hist no hist of cancer, –

Past Hist had small pox when 12 years of age. Had breast amputated at St George's Hospital 6 years ago by Mr Pick-

Pres condition Fairly-well nourished woman, not markedly anaemic. Uterus freely movable, Blood-stained discharge seen issuing from external os, the cervix appears normal.

(a)

Figures 2.7 (a) and (b) Case history of a patient with cancer of the uterus under the care of Mr Jessett in 1894

Name Annie Gardner, | Ward Wilson Bed No 6 | Surgeon Mr F. B. Jessett

DATE.	NOTES.	TREATMENT.	DIET.

Dec 12th Under Ether, Mr Jessett performed vaginal Hysterectomy. Operation lasted exactly an hour, Glass drainage tube used. Vagina packed with Iodoform gauze — [illegible]

On Section the interior of uterus was occupied by a diffuse growth, forming more or less irregular projections on the surface of the mucous membrane —

Patient had gr ¼ suppository of Morphia,

at 12 p.m. blood sucked out of tube with syringe and rubber tube —

Diet: No 1 milk Oi Beef tea Custard and Chicken.

Dec 16th Tube taken out, — Vagina well syringed out and packed with Iodoform gauze

17th Patient doing well, Vagina Syringed out through a Ferguson's Speculum, and packed with Iodoform gauze —

18th Patient very well — Vagina syringed out twice a day —

19th Syringed out twice a day. doing well Fish Diet

20th Temp normal — Vagina well syringed out

Dec 18th Ol. Ricini ℥ss stat.
19th acidi Borici gr x Infus [illegible] ℥
20th Pot Bicarb [illegible] Tinc Hyos ʒss Aq ad ℥i.

Jan 13th 1894 [illegible]

(b)

The Cancer Hospital (Free), Brompton.

WILSON WARD.

Reference........
Path........
P.M........

Under the Care of Mr J.B. Jessett FRCS **, Surgeon.**

Name Mary Rowden *Age* 56 ~~M~~ or ~~S~~ widow *Occupation* –

Where from 16 Victoria street. Whitstable

Disease Secondary Carcinoma *Part affected* – glands supra-clavicular –

Admitted Sept 17th 1894. *Date of Operation* Sept 18th

Discharged Oct 7th 1894 *Result* Convales

Fam History no family history of cancer –
– widow. 2 children, youngest 17. admitted with secondary carcinomatous glands.

June 1892 – The Breast was amputated by Mr Jessett in this Hospital, – patient states she had had growth in breast 9 months before operation. –
In January 1894 had another operation for recurrence of disease – patient has had present disease for the past 4 months.

Pres condition

Fairly healthy and moderately well nourished woman. Heart and lungs normal, above the clavicle and under the pectoral muscle is felt a mass of glands about the size of a pigeon's egg –

Sept 18th. Under Ether. The glands were removed a vertical incision made commencing above the clavicle, the Brachial plexus was found surrounding the growth and had to be dissected off. The growth was very deep surrounded by the neck vessels which were seen in the dissection, another growth was removed under the pectoralis major –

(a)

Figures 2.8 (a) and (b) Case history of a lady with breast cancer treated three times by inadequate surgery

Name	Ward	Bed No	Surgeon

DATE.	NOTES.	TREATMENT.	DIET.
Sept 19th	Had a fairly good night without morphia -		Sept 19 No 1 milk Pudding Beef tea -
Sept 21st	Dressed - drainage tubes removed - wound looks well, some slight brownish discharge squeezed from wound	[illegible]	Sept 20 No 2 Milk Pudding
22	Tube replaced -		
Sept 24	[illegible] Stitches removed - [illegible] about ℥ij of discharge of lower wound, - upper part firmly healed -		

(b)

Figure 2.9 East and west extensions to the Cancer Hospital built by 1883

The chapel was opened by the Bishop of London in 1893 and a garden party was held in celebration. Sir George Meason had appealed to the public for funds for the building and within three months the target of £4,000 had been reached. In his turn Sir Massey Lopes gave money for almost all the chapel fittings. The public have been enduringly generous to this cancer hospital. Later, stained glass windows were contributed in recognition of Sir George Meason and Alexander Marsden's work, while a special fund was started to support the stipend of a chaplain.

Naturally, not everything went so smoothly, and on 9 November 1900 the West London Press recorded an inquest on a lady who had been struck by a picture which had fallen from the wall in her ward. She was 47 years old and suffering from pelvic cancer. The report states that 'the deceased made a great noise and the doctor was called to see her immediately. Witnesses saw no change in her after the accident.' When she died two days later the house sur-

Figure 2.10 The chapel opened in 1893

geon decided on an autopsy as a precaution. The result showed the body was very wasted, the kidneys had been ruptured and the court concluded that while the fall of the picture might have caused the rupture her death was due primarily to the cancer of the womb. 'The husband accepted the findings of the inquest.'

Figure 2.11 Chapel stained glass window in memory of Alexander Marsden

Figure 2.12 Chapel stained glass window in memory of Sir George Meeson

Chapter 3

BETTER TREATMENT AND EARLY RESEARCH (1901–1950)

By the turn of the century the Hospital was particularly interested in supporting research more generously, since 'the Cancer Hospital should be in the forefront for all advancements towards a solution of these questions which so nearly affect the health and happiness of mankind generally'. The start of roentgen or X-ray therapy occurred in 1901 'in otherwise intractable

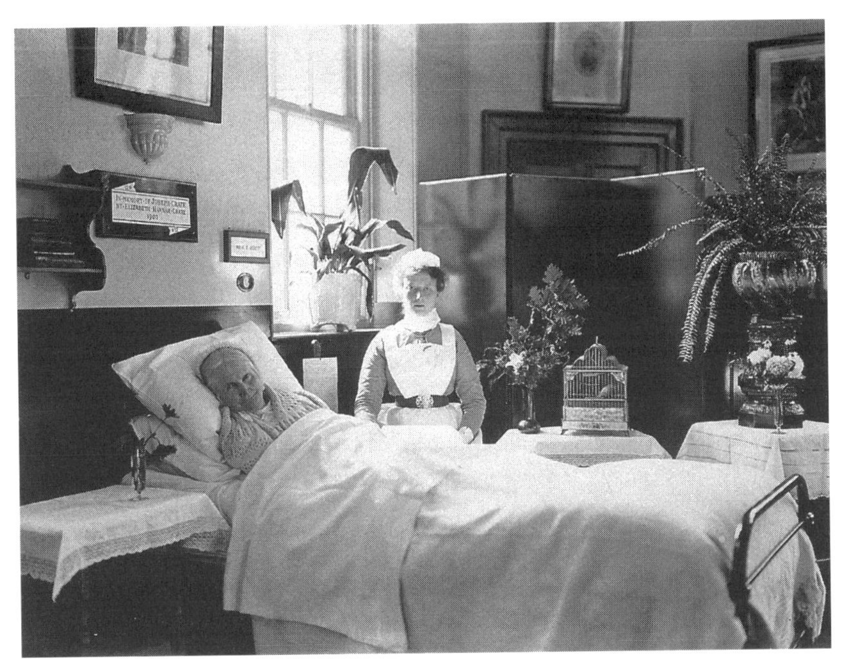

Figure 3.1 Patient and staff in a ward in 1903: the cost of the bed was donated by Elizabeth Clarke

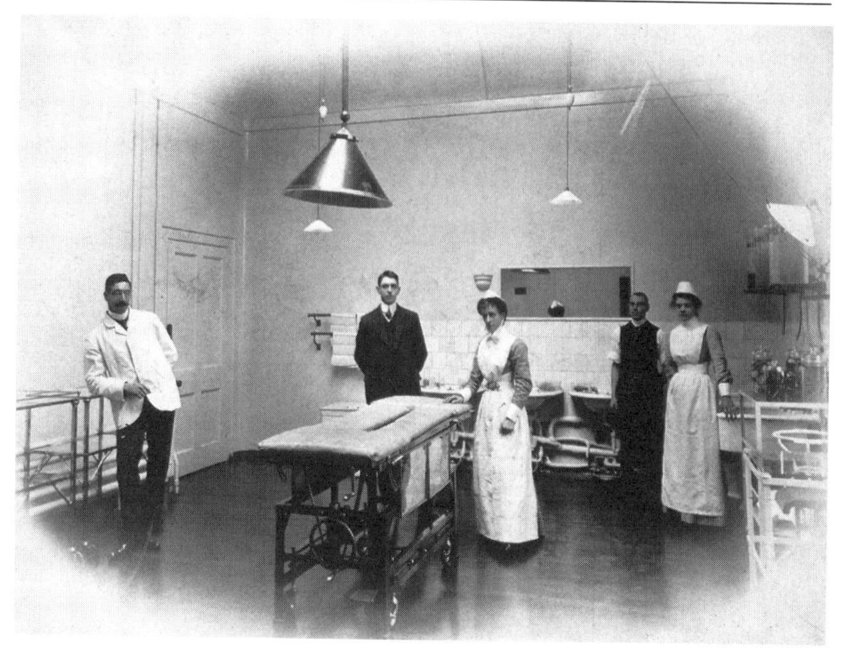

Figure 3.2 The operating theatre in 1904

cases' and some radium was acquired two years later, while a separate pathology and research building was planned. The electrical department was recognized in 1903 when a director, Dr Pollock, was appointed to run the therapeutic and diagnostic areas covered by X-ray and radium. At the same time Dr Alexander Paine became pathologist and undertook much of the planning for the new research building.

By 1908 the Hospital was in a healthy financial state and had acquired a capital fund of more than £266,000 while its annual expenditure amounted to just under £15,000. Other figures show that with 1435 new patients as many as 823 were admitted to the 110 available beds over the year. Patients stayed in the hospital an average of 41 days and 641 operations were performed. The post-operative death rate was 3.27%. Costs for patient care were given as averages – thus in-patient care was £2 12s 10d per patient per week, out-patient visits cost 7s 5d each. The electrical department's expenditure for 1908 was £109 16s 2d about the same amount as was spent on 'wines and spirits'.

Drs Paine and Morgan jointly directed what was now called the Cancer Research and Pathological Department. Predictably, this curious arrangement did not work and the Board decided on a new arrangement when Dr Morgan resigned. Dr Paine became sole Director in the new building, opened in 1910. In his first report to the Board he described testing the usefulness of 'formic acid and its derivatives, ionic medication and radium'. He appears to have run any therapeutic trials, was responsible for the museum and the library and had two staff to support him. At this time Dr (later Lord) Horder was appointed as the first physician, but there is little evidence that he contributed much to the Hospital, medically or otherwise.

At the same time Dr Nolan, the director of the electrical department, reported that its activities included the use of X-rays, radium, galvanism and Faradism, electrolysis and 'high frequency' electric currents. Fifty-two patients appear to have been treated with X-rays during 1907–1908 with 'some benefit'. Radium was applied in 10 cases and was particularly efficacious against rodent ulcers. The department also took 89 diagnostic radiographs and in 1911 took the innovative step of appointing a physicist, a Mr Phillips. Dr Robert Knox became Director in the same year and a new department was planned and opened in 1912, including 20 beds for X-ray and radium therapy. Indeed, at this time both fundamental and clinical foundations were laid for the hospital's remit towards cancer research.

The Hospital seemed to hibernate during the 1914–1918 war and spent a lot of its energy on caring for the war-wounded, for which 70 beds were allocated and 57 were used in 1915. Recovery from the war took a little time but the Hospital did expand its medical staff with a laryngologist and an assistant physician in 1920. Two years later a dental surgeon was appointed and the junior medical staff included two women for the first time.

Dr Leitch, (sometimes spelt Leitz) replaced Dr Paine as Director of the Research Institute. The Annual Report of 1923 comments that the research department 'has shown a very great advance since the appointment to the Directorship of Dr Archibold Leitz'. This suggests that they were less than happy with Dr Paine towards the end of his reign but this may have been unfair, for cancer research was now moving faster in particular in the fields of biochemistry and radiotherapy.

During the 1920s the Board continued to improve and embellish the Hospital, with new operating theatres opened by the Duke of Connaught on 21 October 1925, and new accommodation for ward maids. More land was acquired on Fulham Road, (Numbers 171, 173 and 175) with a view to future developments. The cost was £5,949 7s 2d. A new wing was added at the western end of the main block to house radiotherapy, radiology and an outpatient department. It had two wards designated for private patients – a new direction for the board. This wing was named after Lord Granard, who had given a generous contribution, and was officially opened by HRH Queen Mary on 9 May 1934. The whole project, including apparatus and furniture, cost £150,000 and was completed in 1931.

The development of the Research Institute, radiology and radiotherapy together with medical physics was recognized academically when the University of London inspected the premises and the work in February 1926. It is worth quoting the report at some length.

On radiology they note that: 'The department is well equipped with the most recent types of equipment,' and: 'The Director is Dr Knox who is a man of great keenness and ingenuity.' They had some criticisms with regard to the recognition and resources of physics. They called for more accommodation, 'adequate electrical power', and special equipment as well as a full-time physicist. But there was fulsome praise for the Research Institute. 'Dr Leitch has earned the reputation of being one of the most capable of the pathologists in this country who has devoted himself to the experimental investigation of Cancer.' Again, 'The chemical pathologist is Dr E L Kennaway, an experienced biochemist with a record of discovery over a wide range of chemical pathology.' They concluded that the Hospital should arrange that the scientific director should have a significant voice on the Science Committee, and subject to that they recommended that 'the Cancer Hospital (Free) be provisionally admitted as a School of the University under Statute 74 in the Faculty of Medicine (in Pathology and Radiology) for a period of five years.'

Probably as a result of the University report there was a new sense of urgency to seek improvements to the physics department. When Dr Phillips retired in the same year he was replaced by a more academic physicist, Dr W V Mayneord. Other staff changes included the appointment of women to senior medical positions for the first time. In 1928 the title Professor of Experimental Pathology was conferred on Dr Leitch.

By this time Dr Woodburn Morrison had replaced Dr Knox, and in 1930 he was given the first UK Chair in Radiology at the Cancer Hospital.

In the 1930s staff expansion was rapid, with extra visiting consultants appointed in neurology, dermatology, gynaecology and ophthalmology. At the same time paid research staff were increased – a decision which was partly responsible for the rapid rise in revenue costs to £62,770 in 1932, of which £16,000 was spent on research. In that year radiology supplies, exclusive of radium, cost £6,995 compared to a drugs and supplies budget of £1,612, reflecting the increased use of diagnostic and therapeutic X-rays. By 1937 the Institute had 16 staff and radiology/radiotherapy and physics had nine. By now there were three professors, the latest addition being Dr Cook, a biochemist who joined the Institute in 1934 and gained a Chair a year later. But it wasn't until 1940 that the excellent work of the physics department was recognized, when Val Mayneord was granted the Chair for Physics as applied to Medicine.

On 27 September 1937 the newspapers reported that the Chairman of the Board, Field Marshall Lord Milne, and three other members had resigned. The reasons were obscure and were given simply as a 'rather delicate matter'. Journalists thought that Milne had been given powers to reorganize the institution for financial reasons and had dismissed a member of staff to save money. However, Professor Lamerton, who joined the Institute a year later, reports the 'matter' in question was well known to staff and was referred to as the 'bedbug affair'. Apparently a louse had been found in the bed of a private patient and Milne assumed it had come from the animal house. He dismissed the chief technician for the experimental animals (Jack Marsh). The Director of the Institute was incensed by his behaviour and threatened to resign, as did Alexander Haddow and others, if Marsh was not reinstated. Milne would not back down but the Board did not support him and Milne himself resigned. Mr Marsh went on to spend the whole of his working life at the Institute. In fact he died in the Hospital after 46 years of service, having fallen from a fifth floor window. Many believed that he committed suicide thinking he had cancer, but this was only rumour.

1939 saw the opening of the new Institute building on Fulham Road. This came about when a new member of the Board, Mr Alfred Chester Beatty, offered to buy the former Masonic hospital and to defray much of the cost of equipping the building for experimental work. In total he donated about £50,000, as well as the freehold to the Hospital. It was fortunate that the building was ready just before the second world war started. It housed all experimental pathology, chemistry and the library while radiology and physics remained within the main hospital. The building was named after Chester Beatty, who in 1940 became the Patron of the Hospital.

By this time the Government of the day had recognized the importance of radiation in diagnosis and therapy. In 1940 the Cancer Bill was passed. The Bill supported the establishment of cancer treatment centres around the country, with a commitment of financial support. It made local authorities responsible for arranging a local service. How far the Bill was implemented during the second world war is uncertain, but in the Cancer Hospital progress continued with the purchase of new higher voltage machines. Teaching was expanded, with courses in diagnostic and therapeutic radiography. The danger of bomb damage to the buildings was high, and apart from loss of life there was a risk of scattering radioactivity if the radium store was damaged. It was buried 40 ft below ground for safety. The Hospital acquired a house in Chalfont St Giles called Pollards Wood, (previously the home of Bertam Mills circus) for the purpose of housing patients if the London site had to be evacuated. It was never needed during the war but was used as a convalescent home for some years.

Because many staff were recruited for war service others were temporarily upgraded, including Dr David Smithers who came to the radiology department in 1937. He was made acting director when the incumbent, Dr Flood, joined the Royal

Figure 3.3 Storing radium in a deep pit in the hospital garden

Army Medical Corps (RAMC). By 1943 the Hospital had acquired a first class staff of research radiotherapists and physicists, some doing pioneering work in their fields. Many had entrepreneurial skills and wanted to see expansion and full recognition for their speciality. Radiology was separated from radiotherapy in 1943, but David Smithers wanted to go further.

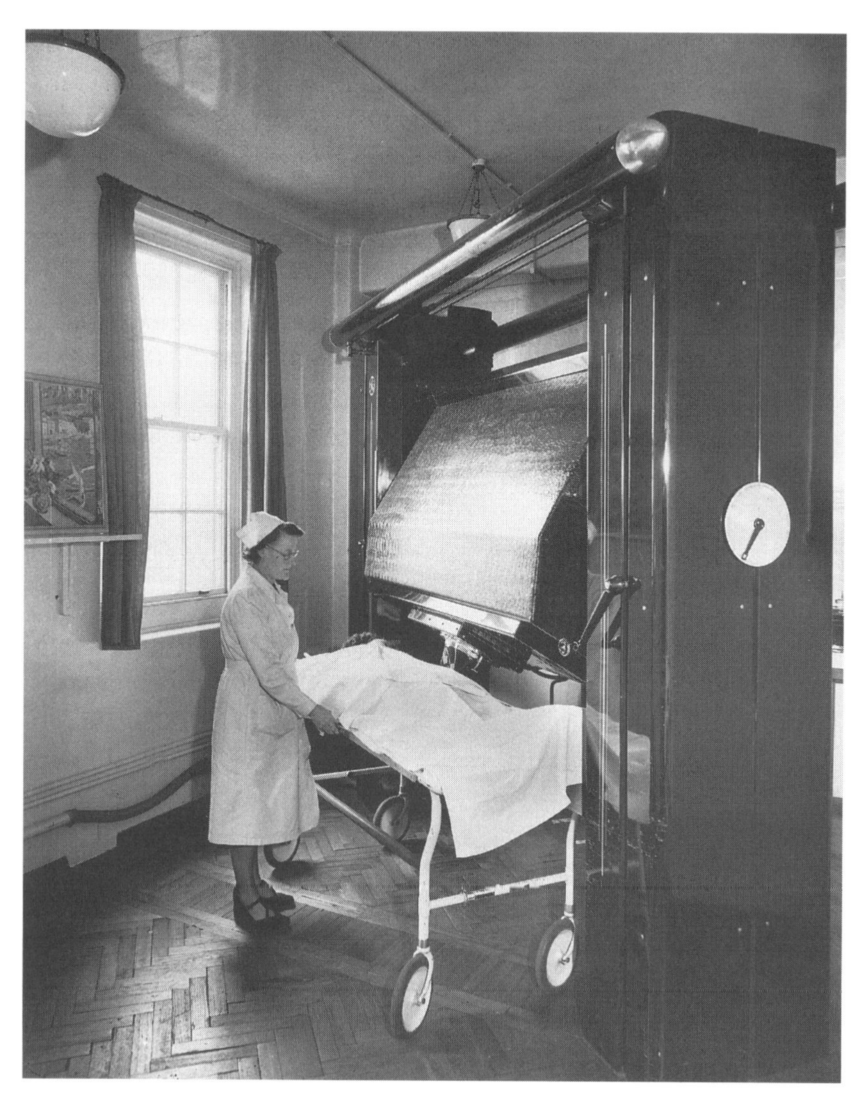

Figure 3.4 Radiotherapy machine, probably 150Kv, with the senior therapeutic radiographer, Miss Reid (about 1950)

He wrote a memorandum, one of many, advising on the concentration of radiotherapy services for London in six centres to assure the availability of expertise and sufficient numbers of patients each year to enhance teaching and the evaluation of the various therapies. He also felt that the surgeons in the Cancer Hospital should not insist on seeing all new patients when some should clearly be directed straight to a radiotherapist. He wanted equal standing with surgeons in the clinic and the ward when, at the time, radiotherapists were only 'in attendance' at surgical out-patients. The Board accepted these suggestions and encouraged the establishment of joint consultation clinics with the Brompton Chest Hospital and the Chelsea Hospital for Women. Later a large network of collaborating hospitals was formed, to the benefit of all concerned.

In 1944 the first report of the Institute to show that chemicals could benefit patients was published. Fifty-three patients were given stilboestrol and benefits were observed in some of those with breast cancer. This was one of the first such reports in the world literature and marked the beginning of the medical treatment of malignancy. Following the election of a Labour government in 1945 the Minister of Health, Mr Bevan, set about implementing plans for a National Health Service. The Bill was passed in 1946 but it took several years to get all the changes in place. The Cancer Hospital was only properly integrated into the system in 1951. Like many other hospitals, the Cancer Hospital was finding it increasingly difficult to support all its functions from donations. Its annual expenditure had risen to £147,712 – the Institute cost £28,859. There was a deficit of £78,648 of income over expenditure so the Hospital only survived by robbing its capital fund.

The Minister decided that the Hospital should be designated a 'Teaching Hospital Ungrouped' but would retain its Board of Governors. The Chairman was chosen by the Minister, as were some members. Resources were allocated by the Minister rather than through a regional committee as for most other hospitals, but the Government would only pay for the patient care, not the research. This posed a serious difficulty for the Board, and after much discussion with the University of London, Department of Health and the newly-formed Postgraduate Medical Federation it was forced to accept that the Institute and Hospital should separate managerially, while all academic work be done as a member of the British Postgraduate Medical Federation via the Institute. The articles of association of the Institute were finalized in 1954 but government money dried up in 1951, at which time the Hospital handed over £450,000 of its endowment funds and its research funds of £30,000 to the Institute, as well as the Pollards Wood building and grounds and the Chester Beatty building in Fulham Road. The two institutions also agreed on the proportion of hospital activity which would be funded by the Institute, by virtue of the research done in each department, as the Ministry of Health would not do so. The agreed proportions were physics 100% research funding, pathology 10%, medical records 50%, all other hospital departments 10%. For radiotherapy some salaries (including the professor) were the responsibility of the Institute, but it did not cover the activity or capital costs. Last, all the costs of the Chester Beatty laboratories and Pollards Wood were funded by research sources. Having split from the Hospital the Institute had to find its own sources of money, although there was a government commitment that some money would come from the Medical Research Council. Other sources included the Cancer Research Campaign and the Anna Fuller Trust (USA) as well as public donation.

The split was momentous and almost certainly a mistake. Although collaboration and joint endeavour has been well maintained it deprived the Hospital of all its academic staff, both in terms of their contracts, responsibilities and credit for their research. On the Institute side it meant that Hospital staff had no remit to support research in the clinic and could not use the Hospital's well known reputation to encourage public support. This was the beginning of the perception, common in the outside medical world, that the Cancer Hospital was there for service only and did no research. In fact the Hospital sees the Institute of Cancer Research as its laboratory research arm for fundamental studies and supports the ICR in bringing any relevant advances to the clinic. This arrangement has always worked well and continues so to do. Thus in looking at the work of either organization one must take into account the contribution made by its sister institution.

Chapter 4

HOSPITAL EXPANSION AND POLITICAL BATTLES (1951–1995)

By the time the Hospital and Institute were managerially separated there were already plans for expansion of buildings, especially with regard to radiotherapy and radioisotope research. In 1948 discussions began with the Ministry of Health for a suitable site. The Hospital wanted to build on the south side of the London site where there was an old Catholic school (Oratory School). However the Ministry was reluctant to allow this on the grounds that more radioactive sources should not be concentrated in central London. There was also the possibility that such expansion might interfere with similar plans to extend and rebuild the Brompton Chest Hospital. The Cancer Hospital's bid was turned down by the Government; instead a site in Horley, 30 miles away, was offered. This was too distant from London and was inappropriate as an area for radiation research. After much further discussion a new site was found in Sutton, Surrey, 13 miles from the parent hospital. In 1950 Professors Mayneord and Smithers, the prime movers of the expansion, agreed the proposal, perhaps fearing that if they turned it down expansion would never be permitted. The Sutton option was a good one because its sloping site allowed for relatively cheap building arrangements to contain radiation sources safely. However the Ministry had a hidden agenda, to move the whole of the Cancer Hospital to Sutton in due course and close the London end. Although the Sutton site was agreed by all parties in 1950 plans for the building were not submitted until 1953. The first phase was to include accommodation for 150 beds, at a cost of £1,198,000. Building was well under way by 1955 and was officially opened by Her Majesty Queen Elizabeth II on 20 May 1963. It took another seven years before phase two begun, encompassing more beds, operating theatres and a special reverse-barrier nursing ward for patients having bone marrow transplants. There fol-

Figure 4.1 HM Queen Elizabeth II at the opening of the new hospital in Sutton in 1963 (Professor Smithers is on the left and the Chairman of the Board of Governors on the right)

Figure 4.2 The completed Sutton building

lowed almost continuous expansion of activity, often housed in temporary buildings. The Institute transferred several departments to Sutton, including drug development, radiobiology and epidemiology. Indeed what had started as a national research centre for radiation research became a hospital with associated radiation and other research laboratories.

Following the introduction of the National Health Service the Hospital discussed a change of name because it was felt that the word cancer was too frightening and a deterrent to patients. Many suggestions were made and rejected but finally it was agreed that the Royal Marsden Hospital was the most appropriate. The Royal Charter had been granted by Edward VIII, and in 1962 a Board member applied to the College of Arms for a Grant of Arms. It was designed by the College of Arms and paid for by some Board members and was granted just in time for the opening of the Surrey branch. The shield bears the colours of the Arms of Chelsea (red and gold) and of Sutton (blue and white), is divided by a line in the form of an 'M' for Marsden and shows the staff of Aesculapias for healing.

Edward the Eighth, by the Grace of God of Great Britain, Ireland and the British Dominions beyond the Seas King, Defender of the Faith, Emperor of India.

To all to whom these Presents shall come, Greeting!

Whereas by Royal Charter bearing date the 31st day of May, 1910, the President and Governors of The Cancer Hospital (Free) were incorporated under the name The Cancer Hospital (Free):

And Whereas the said Corporation have presented unto Us their Petition praying for the grant of a Supplemental Charter whereby the prefix " Royal " shall be added to the style and title of the said Corporation so that it may be known as " The Royal Cancer Hospital (Free) " :

Now know ye that as well upon the prayer of the said Corporation as also of Our own special Grace certain knowledge and mere motion We do hereby grant and ordain that the name of the said Corporation shall henceforth be " The Royal Cancer Hospital (Free)."

And We do will that this Our Charter shall be deemed to be supplemental to the said Charter and shall be construed and have effect accordingly.

In Witness whereof We have caused these Our Letters to be made Patent.

Witness Ourself at Westminster the *first* day of *December* in the *first* year of Our reign.

By Warrant under The King's Sign Manual.

Schuster

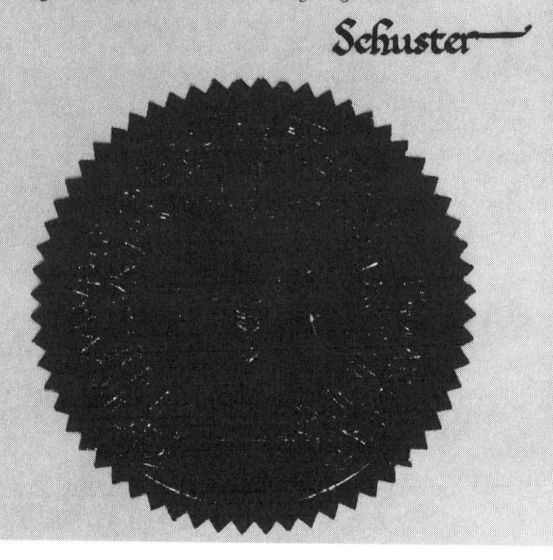

Figure 4.3 Grant of the Royal Charter by HM Edward VIII in 1910

Figure 4.4 Grant of Arms to the Hospital in 1962

Two bald coots come from the arms of William Marsden and the crown denotes the 'Royal'. The stag's head on the crest is from the arms of the Baroness Burdett-Coutts, while the bee is from the arms of Sir Alfred Chester Beatty, who endowed the Institute. The lightning streaks symbolize radiation. Last, the supporters, unicorn and owl, stand for watchfulness by day and night while the crabs they trample underfoot are for cancer. The motto is taken from that of Marsden, namely 'Labor Omnia Vincit'.

The centenary of the founding of the Hospital was celebrated in 1951 with an exhibition of this history and achievements of the Hospital and the Institute. Her Royal Highness the Duchess of Gloucester opened the celebrations which

Figure 4.5 Coat of arms

included a dinner and staff ball. In the same year the Government first introduced charges for prescriptions, only three years after the NHS began, and the Secretary of the Hospital thought this was inconsistent with the idea of a free hospital for poor people. He refused to implement the charge, initially 1 shilling, and after many attempts to persuade him to conform the Ministry of Health sent a representative to his office one day with an order to close the Hospital down if he did not comply. He had to give in.

Because of the change from full responsibility for its own affairs to a Ministry directed NHS hospital the Board now spent

Figure 4.6 The Medical Committee about 1950. Front row from left to right: Mrs Rigby Jones (radiotherapist) 2. Dr Vaile (anaesthetist) 3. (not known) 4. Lord Horder (physician) 5. Chairman of the Board of Governors 6. Mr C Shattuck (surgeon) 7. Mr R Ledlie (surgeon) 8. Mr Victor Pinkham (Hospital secretary) 9. Dr Thompson Hancock (physician) 10. Dr Chester (anaesthetist) Second row: 1. Dr Jarman (anaesthetist) 2. Mr R Raven (surgeon) 3. (not known) 4. Dr J W Whittick (pathologist) 5. Professor D Smithers (radiotherapist) 6. Mr Coffin (dental surgeon) 7. Dr Gordon (dermatologist) 8. Professor W V Mayneord (medical physics) 9. Dr J Harman (physician) 10. Dr M Lederman (radiotherapist) 11. Dr Stevenson (radiologist) 12. Professor A Haddow (Director of the Institute of Cancer Research) Back row: 1. Dr Cledwyn Lewis (anaesthetist) 2. Mr Alan Hunt (surgeon) 3. Mr W Mill (surgeon) 4. (not known) 5. (not known) 6. Mr M. Harmer (surgeon)

much of its time asking permission from government to appoint senior staff and to beg for money. It began to discuss trivia rather than strategy and medical matters rarely surfaced. However it did agree to the formation of a clinical research department, to be headed by a director, preferably a professor. This was first mooted in 1956 and in 1960 endowment money was allocated, but it took another two years to appoint the senior general physician, Dr Thompson Hancock, as Director. There seems to have been no competition for the post; Hancock only worked part-time and had no research experience. Surprisingly, the Institute's clinical research department was not included, despite the fact that it was the main source of clinical research at the time. This rather fragile and ineffective department continued until a Chair of Medicine was eventually created and Professor Bondy, from Yale University Medical School, was appointed in 1972. Bondy did not know the UK health system and he was an endocrinologist rather than a cancer physician but he did bring a few young, talented staff into the department and established a senior lecturer post. When he left in 1977 there was strong competition for his post and much argument about the type of person, clinician or experimentalist, who should be appointed. Eventually Timothy McElwain took the post and held it with distinction until his untimely death in 1990. Since then the Institute, which remains the prime mover for all academic posts in the Hospital, has been unwilling to make a new appointment.

Ever since its inception the concept of a specialist cancer hospital has been resisted by civil servants and the undergraduate hospitals, especially their doctors. Even Queen Victoria refused to support an institution for the treatment of one disease. But while the Queen changed her mind and the monarchs who came after her all gave personal support, others have remained adamantly opposed. This opposition became overt after the NHS came into being. It was made clear in a quote from *Hansard* for 17 March 1957 which stated that: 'The policy of the Ministry of Health based on the advices of the

Standing Committee on cancer and radiotherapy was not to treat cancer as a speciality and not to base the treatment of cancer in special hospitals but in general hospitals.' This despite the fact that the trend internationally at that time was to develop "stand-alone" institutions. Indeed the famous Memorial Hospital and its associated Sloane Kettering Research Center in New York were built on the model pioneered by the Royal Marsden Hospital and the Institute for Cancer Research.

In 1961–2 there was a move by the postgraduate hospitals of London, of which the RMH was one, to come together on one or two sites. Several imaginative plans were put forward, including one to build on a vacant site of an old fever hospital in west London. Each hospital and its associated institute was to have its own building but would share certain common services. Such a complex would have given the country a medical centre to rival what became the National Institutes of Health in Bethesda, Maryland, USA. Enoch Powell, then Minister of Health, stated on 21 June 1961 that there would be two sites, one in west London and one in Holborn. The Pickering Report confirmed this. A project manager was appointed in 1963 but he resigned in 1966. The *Sunday Times* reported him as saying: 'My job is to plan hospitals which are going to admit patients, not merely to plan plans.' (1 May 1996). The scheme faded away, despite the enthusiasm of the hospitals involved. Meanwhile it blighted development of their own buildings for several years and probably made inevitable the incorporation of at least the smaller ones into the powerful undergraduate hospitals. A subsequent series of reports and NHS reorganizations sought to bring all the postgraduate hospitals within the management arrangements of the rest of NHS, but they did not fit easily with the general regional scheme because of their national appeal to patients. The relevant minister kept on delaying a decision to alter their status. Thus in the 1974 reorganization these hospitals were allowed to remain outside the general plan for 'at least five years'. This meant that instead of being accountable to a regional authority the Special Health Authorities (SHAs), as they were called, were accountable centrally to the Department of Health.

As a result, the widespread disillusion with the bureaucracy of the regional system did not affect the SHA but did add a further source of friction between it and the rest of the NHS hospitals. Others saw the SHA as privileged and believed it had an unfair share of resources. The SHA in its turn continued to feel threatened and was constantly required to justify itself and its status.

From 1980 a flurry of reports, commissions and plans were put forward for London hospital services but no action was taken by politicians. There were, however, some rather ominous signs of continuing hostility. The Department of Health did not support the proposed amalgamation or shared radiotherapy service between Charing Cross Hospital and the London branch of the Royal Marsden Hospital, and it fell through. Then the Department rejected the claim that the RMH with its Institute was the National Cancer Centre. Finally, when the latest reorganization of the NHS took place the SHAs were the last to be allowed to become independent Trusts – after the market had largely been carved up by others.

Earlier there had been further surveys of London medical services, including the Tomlinson Report, and the Cancer Committee Report chaired by Dr Paine, a radiotherapist from Oxford. Both recommended amalgamation of the Royal Marsden Hospital in Sutton, with an undergraduate teaching hospital and the closure of the London branch. As before the Board strongly resisted these suggestions and pointed out that the relationship of the Hospital to the Institute was crucial to its proper function. Furthermore, the Institute was an independent body which could not be dictated to by government. By 1993 bids for Trust status were allowed for SHAs but the Government directed the Royal Marsden Hospital to bid on its own account. Within a few weeks the Government changed its mind and demanded a joint bid with the National Heart and

Lung Hospital, previously the Brompton Hospital. Apart from the fact that the two were sited next door to one another they had little in common. A merger would not have produced great savings, so within weeks the Department changed its mind yet again and told the RMH to produce another stand-alone Trust application. By this time the hospital management were becoming quite proficient at writing Trust applications and on this occasion were successful. The RMH became an NHS Trust on 1 April 1994, and perhaps against the better judgement of the Secretary of State, the Fulham Road branch was reprieved. In her words on 10 February 1994: 'There has been much speculation about the future of the Royal Marsden. I am pleased to announce that it too will become an NHS Trust from April. Together with the generous initial funding which, as a former SHA, the Marsden will receive, this decision gives it every opportunity to shape its own future responding to patient choice.'

Many operational changes took place after 1960, including the expansion of consultant posts for psychiatry, orthopaedics, plastic surgery and joint posts with St. George's Hospital so that the SHA could provide all radiotherapy services to both hospitals. There were also joint surgical posts with St. Bartholomew's Hospital and one physician, Professor Hamilton Fairley, who came on a part-time basis to the Sutton branch. The first ethical committee was formed in 1973. A crèche was built at Sutton for the children of staff, while in London staff shared the crèche facilities provided by the Brompton Hospital. Staff were also supported by an occupational health department.

From 1966 the Board and management became increasingly concerned about the rapidly rising cost of drugs and costs have been greater than budget ever since. To try to tackle the problem the Hospital gave the medical division the drugs budget data and later transferred responsibility for controlling drug expenditure to a multidisciplinary Drugs and Therapeutics Committee. While drug costs have continued to rise, the Committee has been successful in controlling the irrational use of drugs and has found savings in bulk buying. It has also taken decisions on behalf of the whole hospital as to whether a certain drug should be purchased, based only on the best available scientific evidence.

Other developments included the promotion and development of multidisciplinary clinical units to enhance the quality of treatment by combining specialist skills. The first units were formed *ad hoc* and concerned the care of haematological, germ cell and ovarian tumours together with soft tissue sarcoma. But at first management paid little more than lip-service to the unit system and some consultants thought they need only change the name of their junior team to be a unit and fulfil the criteria. The point of the unit system was to collaborate and agree with colleagues on how care should be delivered. Discussions between peer groups were essential. These arrangements did not suit everyone and there was quite an argument between the 'generalists' and the gynaecological unit when a radiotherapy consultant post became vacant. The unit wanted a person who would confine his work to gynaecological cancers but the division of radiotherapy thought he should be free to have a general radiotherapy practice. After much debate the unit view prevailed and has not been seriously challenged for subsequent posts, especially now when all sides of the hospital support the unit system enthusiastically.

Two other important changes occurred in the 1980s: a department of clinical endocrinology headed by Mitchell Dowsett was formed (1987) and in the same year a Chair in haematology was established and Professor Daniel Catowsky took up the post.

Chapter 5

SURGICAL AND PATHOLOGICAL PROGRESS

From its inception until the 1930s when other disciplines began to have more influence the Hospital was run essentially by surgeons. In the 19th century surgery held sway, despite the fact that operating possibilities were limited, first by the lack of anaesthetics and then by the absence of antisepsis. In fact between 1851 and 1862 only 57 operations were performed, although during that time 4,804 patients were seen. After an anaesthetist was appointed in 1874 this number rose to 449 by 1875. Antiseptic techniques were introduced a year later enabling surgeons to became bolder and operations more frequent and more extensive. In the last 20 years of the century the removal of drainage nodes from, for example, breast cancer cases was common and some surgeons were advocating amputation for tumours of the limbs. But in the Cancer Hospital the surgeons seemed, in general, to be rather cautious. Whether this caution was born of a knowledge of poor outcome or whether they were old-fashioned in outlook is uncertain but their Annual Reports suggest the latter, and they continued to favour local removal of tumour by the knife or by cautery as late as 1890.

In 1884 the surgeons were Drs William Marsden, Snow, Purcell, Lamb, Bailey and Bourne. Not one was full-time and this group now comprised the newly formed Medical Committee. In the same year serious problems arose in the relationship between one surgeon and his colleagues and this lead to a widely publicized and damaging libel action. Two surgical posts were advertised, surgeon and assistant surgeon, and there were several applicants including a young man called Jennings who applied for both posts but failed to get either. Instead, a Mr Jessett and Mr Stoneham were appointed. However, a few months later Mr Jennings joined the staff as an extra assistant surgeon without any post having been advertised and without discussion with the Medical Committee. How this happened remains unclear but it seems that one of Jennings' sponsors was the honorary treasurer. In any event the medical staff were not pleased and Jennings was not made welcome. Indeed, he reported that no one shook his hand and he was not allocated any beds for his patients for several months. Later he was given five beds. From that moment controversy seemed to abound – always involving Mr Jennings. In July 1886 a letter was sent to the Board by the Medical Committee saying, in effect, that they could not get on with him and asking that he be requested to resign. The Board rejected the request and the letter was withdrawn. Earlier Jennings had asked for promotion to full surgeon but it was denied by his colleagues, although they did increase his bed allocation to 10. Why did they dislike him so much? Clearly he was a contentious individual and resisted most suggestions made by other surgeons, but there was no suggestion that he was incompetent and there is little doubt that there was a very cosy relationship between the rest of the medical staff, who do not seem to have been committed to modern methods. At some point a circular was received, apparently from the Anti-Vivisection Society, accusing Jennings of being a 'horrible man in doing some experiments on animals'. Jennings thought the contents showed that information had come from a member of the hospital staff because of the inside knowledge it displayed. When the Medical Committee members denied all knowledge of the piece Jennings seemed not to accept their denial and when asked to accept it he said: 'I do not think it is a question I should answer.'

The stage was set for further confrontation – it seems the surgeons could not wait to find some reason to be rid of

Jennings. An opportunity arose when he asked for a consultation about a case. This was common practice in the hospital; indeed there was a rule that if major surgery was to be performed in a 'serious' case then the agreement of his peers was mandatory, although it appears to have been only rarely requested. Mrs Clarke had a tumour on the arm in the site of an old burn which she had suffered when she was 8 years old. The tumour had been present for eight years and several surgeons outside the Cancer Hospital had advised amputation. When Snow, Purcell and Jessett saw the patient they said they could not assess the case because the tumour was covered with an ointment, which they ordered to be removed. They understood Mrs Clarke was to have an amputation of the arm which they thought was unnecessary. Jennings first reordered the ointment and then took the patient to the operating theatre and would have operated had Mrs Clarke not refused at the last minute. As soon as Snow and others knew that Jennings planned the surgery despite their advice they wrote to the Chairman of the Board setting out the facts. They said that it was 'not a case for any serious interference with the limb until another less severe operation than amputation has been tried'. The letter was signed by Snow, Purcell and Jessett. As a result Mr Jennings was suspended immediately and two weeks later was dismissed by the Board. In February Jennings brought a libel action against Snow. The subsequent hearing at the High Court brought the Hospital a lot of bad publicity and resulted in the loss of subscribers and some governors. After the three-day hearing Jennings won the case and was granted costs and £10 in damages. But trouble did not end there. Jennings, by virtue of his 2 guinea contribution to the Hospital, was able to attend the Annual General Meeting, and did so in 1889 and 1890. Again he and some supporters complained, first about the Board's failure to reinstate him, and second about the unusual practice of giving honoraria (up to 150 guineas) to some surgeons. He also wanted Snow, rather than the Hospital, to pay the legal costs of the libel case – about

£600. Again he lost against a Chairman and Committee who found money from a legacy to pay the charges. Jessett in his turn accused Jennings of trying to woo patients away from the Hospital to attend him privately in Brook Street.

After this harmony returned, but no surgical innovation was visible and it was not until the turn of the century that modern surgical methods were evident in the Cancer Hospital practice. It is possible that having Jennings on the staff would have been a good thing after all.

Charles Ryall, who was appointed house surgeon in 1897, became full surgeon at the turn of the century and was joined by Ernest Miles, who became famous for his abdomino-pelvic approach to large bowel cancer. Both were later knighted for their surgical work.

In 1952 a new surgeon was appointed for urological work for the first time, and David Wallace took the post. He was a surgeon who fully understood the benefits of collaboration with Institute scientists in attempts to answer questions about human cancer. He sparkled with ideas and enthusiasm, illustrated first by producing one of the earliest medical films for training surgeons in the new, simple prostatectomy operation. He worked closely with histopathologists, especially Roger Pugh at the Institute of Urology, and Noel Gowing at the Hospital. Together they formulated a system of grading for bladder tumours on the basis of surgical findings and histopathological features which became accepted around the world. He also worked closely with radiotherapists, especially Professor Smithers and Julian Bloom. They organized one of the first multicentre clinical trials as well as conducting single centre studies on best radiotherapy practice for bladder and testicular cancers. He also worked with Institute staff on epidemiological studies into the causes of bladder cancer and was able to show the greater incidence of this cancer in people employed in the rubber industry. His labours were honoured internationally but he was underrated in his own country. Indeed, when he retired from the Marsden and went to Riyadh

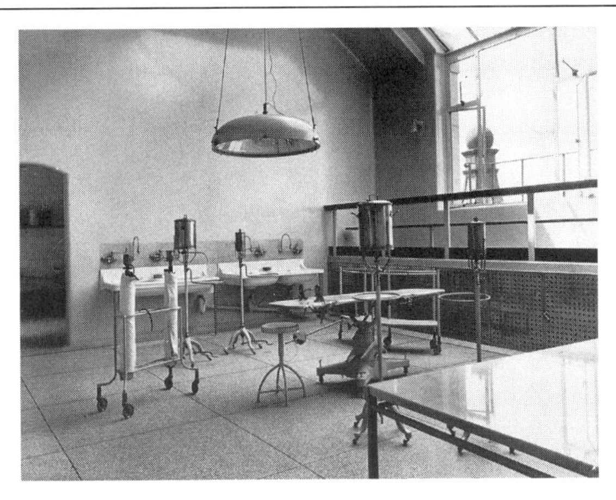

Figure 5.1 An operating theatre 1925

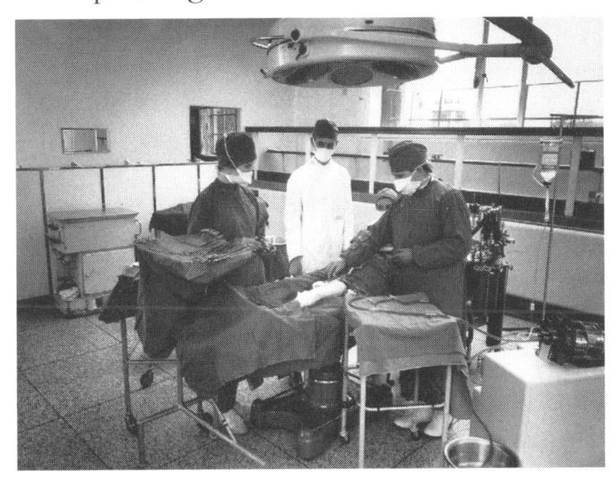

Figure 5.2 An operating theatre 1962

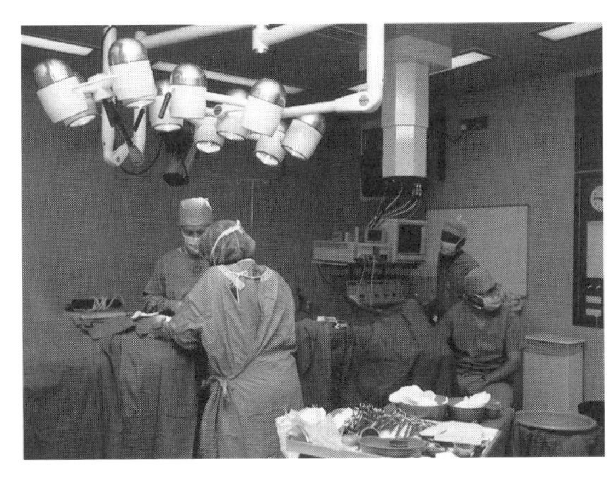

Figure 5.3 An operating theatre 1992

Figure 5.4 Mr David Wallace

as Professor of Surgery he was awarded a CBE for 'diplomatic and political work' rather than for his medical contributions.

Another surgeon with good ideas and a penchant for new methods was Peter Greening (appointed 1952). An excellent technician and diagnostician, he came to concentrate his efforts on the management of breast cancer. He worked closely with Institute clinicians on early trials of hormone and cytotoxic drug therapy and he set up the first UK screening unit for well women who were worried about the possibility that they were developing breast cancer. The unit was criticized for not being able to show whether screening was of real value but a great deal was learned about the best tests to apply and how to interpret them. Later Greening began to advocate less radical surgery for breast cancer but he was not sufficiently

Figure 5.5 Mr Peter Greening

disciplined to do or to organize clinical trials that would convince others.

In the 1970s it was apparent that more radical surgery or even radiotherapy was not the answer to the cure of most cancers. Rather surprisingly it was at this time the Hospital and Institute decided that a Chair in surgery was appropriate. The first holder was Gerald Westbury, who came from the Westminster Hospital and Medical School where he already had a good reputation as an operator and a teacher. His main surgical interest in the cancer field was soft tissue sarcoma. These are rare tumours but a large practice had been built at

Figure 5.6 Professor 'Charlie' Westbury

the Marsden, although the clinical group involved lacked surgical expertise which Westbury now supplied. He was also the driving force behind a plan to build new, state-of-the-art, operating theatres at the London branch. Discussions started in 1983 but it took two years to achieve Ministry approval and another seven before they were built.

While histopathology is now central to the diagnosis of most cancers it was not until the early 1900s that the Cancer Hospital took the subject seriously. In the legal battle of the surgeons in 1889 (Jennings vs Jessett) it was not considered important by either side, although a biopsy seems to have been taken. In its early days the Institute was headed by pathologists, but these men were not concerned with human diagnostic problems but rather with ideas concerning causes of the disease. The first diagnostician was appointed in 1908 but the first notable histopathologist was a Dr Piney, who joined in 1928 and wrote a well-known book on the pathology of cancer. At this time the importance of pathology gained rapid recognition. During 1938 more than 1,000 patients supplied specimens for microscopic diagnostic purposes. Dr Willis was another first-class pathologist. He wrote and published a book on metastatic disease which was a classic, before he left to go to Leeds as professor. Whittick was then appointed. He was a good diagnostician but a quiet and retiring man who did not publish his work. He was succeeded by Noel Gowing, who wrote several books on cancer diagnosis and also ran a successful postgraduate course for consultants where difficult slides were sent to participants for their opinions. The cases were then discussed with the group during a week-long meeting at the Hospital. Gowing was made professor in 1971.

In most hospitals in the UK histopathology has been a Cinderella subject. In part this is because its practitioners are often quiet and not political, so their departments have tended to be hidden away in some corner of the grounds – often within inadequate and neglected buildings. The Royal Marsden Hospital was no exception. When radiotherapy wanted to expand its premises in 1948 pathology was rehoused in 'temporary accommodation' in a single-storey block commonly known as 'the huts'. Even when the Sutton site was opened in 1962 histopathology depended on the hospitality of the Institute for its accommodation. Despite these problems diagnostic excellence and good postgraduate teaching have been central to the work of this department.

Chapter 6

THE INSTITUTE OF CANCER RESEARCH

As soon as the Hospital could see some hope of advancing knowledge of cancer by laboratory research it built a separate block within the hospital grounds. The Cancer Hospital Research Institute was born in 1909 and the new building was opened by the Duke of Connaught in 1911. The first Director

Figure 6.1 The Duke of Connaught with some nurses after opening the Hospital Research Institute in 1911

Figure 6.2 The Masonic Hospital in Fulham Road bought by Sir Alfred Chester Beatty to house the Hospital's new research activity. (This building was originally built as the Chelsea Hospital for Women founded in 1880)

was Alexander Paine, previously one of two pathologists on the Hospital staff. He had much to do with the design of the building. Initially the Institute consisted of two departments, pathology and radiology the ('electrical department'). Later a department of physics was added.

There had been some research within the Hospital before the Institute was formed in that a Dr Plimmer had looked into possible causes of cancer. Plimmer was appointed in 1888 and at first he favoured the idea of a protozoal cause of cancer and described cellular inclusions later known as Plimmer bodies (1892). Later he thought that fungi of the yeast group might be involved. Plimmer left the hospital in 1904 and later became an FRS and Professor of Comparative Pathology at Imperial College of Science. Dr Alexander Paine is chiefly remembered for his bacteriological research on rheumatism. Although he did not make any noteworthy addition to knowledge of cancer he appointed excellent researchers to the Institute, including Charles Singer, who investigated gastric function and blood pressure in cancer patients and went on to become a distinguished medical historian. The others were E H Kettle, who wrote an important textbook on the pathology of tumours; G W Nicholson, who moved to Guy's Hospital in the Chair of Morbid Anatomy; S B Schryler, an organic chemist, later Professor of Biochemistry at Imperial College; and Jack Drummond, another distinguished chemist. Most of them were later made Fellows of the Royal Society.

The second Director, appointed in 1921, was Archibald Leitch, whose training in cancer included a post as house surgeon at the Hospital and pathology at the Middlesex Hospital, as well as a stint as Director of Cancer Research at Dundee. Almost at once Leitch began experimental research with his colleague Ernest Kennaway into the carcinogenic effects of tars and oils in animals. This approach was influenced, no doubt, by the work at the Imperial Cancer Research Fund laboratories and the discovery in Japan that cancer could be produced by the application of coal tar to the skin. Leitch showed that shale oil and lubricants were carcinogenic and thus added to the knowledge of the cause of mule-spinners' cancer. He also noted that cancers could arise in treated animals long after stopping the application of the carcinogen. In recognition of his work the University of London granted him the first Chair of Experimental Pathology at the Cancer Hospital in 1928.

The third Director was Ernest Kennaway, who stayed in the post from 1931 to 1946. He continued the work on carcinogenic substances and was fortunate to have as a colleague W V Mayneord, the Hospital's medical physicist. Kennaway discovered that chemical agents, especially the polycyclic aro-

Figure 6.3 Sir Ernest Kennaway FRS, Director of the Institute 1931–1946

matic hydrocarbons, were carcinogenic in animals. Further, he found that some tars were fluorescent in ultra-violet light, while Mayneord was able to demonstrate that their fluorescent spectra were characteristic of carcinogenic substances. This enabled the distinguished pair of researchers to track down the actual compounds which produced the tumours. Kennaway received many honours for his work, including the FRS (1934), the Royal medal of that society (1941) and a knighthood in 1947. In 1955 he wrote an article in the *British Medical Journal* (ii.749) explaining how the offending compound in coal-tar was found and the part played by each of his colleagues. Kennaway suffered greatly from Parkinson's disease, which was already apparent when he became Director. A former colleague, J W Cook, said of him: 'The intense driving force of his willpower must have contributed in large measure to his mastery of the increasingly adverse circumstances of his later years.' To add to his problems Kennaway suffered a serious accident in 1946 and retired from the Institute. Nevertheless he continued to conduct research at St. Bartholomew's Hospital until his death in 1958.

In 1926, as a result of the quality work of the Institute the University of London came to inspect its premises and staff. Its favourable report led to recognition of the pathology and radiology departments as being of academic standing and, during 1928–9, the granting of two Chairs to Ernest Kennaway (experimental pathology) and to Woodburn-Morrison (radiology).

It was the combined work of James Cook, I Heiger, Kennaway and Mayneord that identified 3:4 benzpyrene as the major carcinogen in coal tar (published in 1932). This was an important discovery which greatly influenced the work of a young scientist in Edinburgh called Alexander Haddow. Haddow was a trained microbiologist but was increasingly interested in cancerous growth, in particular carcinogenesis, so it was natural that he began to collaborate with James Cook, using carcinogenic hydrocarbons to look at their effects on growth. He found that they did inhibit the growth of implanted sarcomata in animals and he wrote a letter to the *Lancet* linking chemical and radiation carcinogenesis to tumour inhibition. His research led Haddow to look for work with a total commitment to cancer research, and he found it in the Chester Beatty Research Institute, which he joined in 1936. The bright team already there included Cook, Kennaway and Mayneord. Their work was complemented by that of Haddow and, having identified the nature of some carcinogens, the team's interest began to shift towards the possibility of controlling cancer growth by chemical means.

The move of the Institute in 1939 to the old Freemasons Hospital site – brought about by the generosity of Sir Alfred Chester Beatty – greatly improved the facilities for research workers. These were further enhanced when in 1948 the Hospital gave over the whole of the site at Pollards Wood for research.

It is interesting to recall that Kennaway and his wife, who also worked at the Institute, began to look at the incidence of cancer of the lung and larynx as early as 1936. They noted that the incidence was rising sharply and further study suggested a causal relationship with cigarette smoking (*British Journal of Cancer* 1947).

Kennaway was succeeded as Director by Alexander Haddow, who had already published at least one paper on regression of human tumours by chemical means. He steered research much more in the direction of finding and synthesizing growth inhibiting anticancer agents. Haddow had had a rather stormy relationship with Kennaway. Both were headstrong and uncompromising and Haddow felt his work did not have the support it deserved from Kennaway. Haddow was much-loved by his employees, who he cherished, but his relations with those above him were often tempestuous. So when the Institute split from the Royal Marsden Hospital due to the arrival of the NHS he must have been pleased to be rid of the control of the Hospital Board. However he fared little better with the Institute of Cancer Research committee of management, who seemed to him to interfere too much in the running of the Institute which he considered his business alone. In one obit-

Figure 6.4 The renovated Chester Beatty Building for cancer research opened in 1939

Figure 6.5 Sir Alfred Chester Beatty

uary it was reported that in a rejoinder to a finance committee Haddow said that it was their function to find the money and his to spend it. This attitude could only be sustained by a man of such ability that the record of his achievements could not be questioned. In fact his reign (1946–1969) covered perhaps the most productive period of the Institute's history so far.

Having set out to produce anticancer agents of value in man Haddow recognized the need for a clinical arm to test drugs in the clinic. He appointed David Galton in 1947 to head a small department of clinicians conducting clinical trials of new drugs coming from the Institute of Cancer Research (ICR) or elsewhere. This was the first clinical chemotherapy group in Europe. Many thought that the move was premature, but time has again proved that his instinct was correct.

The position of the radiotherapy and physics departments was complicated as far as the ICR Director was concerned, for both were headed by professors and both were housed within the Hospital, although they were Institute departments. This

Figure 6.6 Sir Alexander Haddow FRS, Director of the Institute 1946–1969

sometimes led to conflict, especially between Haddow and David Smithers, the Professor of radiotherapy. Smithers was a power to be reckoned with inside the Hospital. Occasionally one would oppose the plans of the other simply because of the source. Despite these caveats the period of Haddow's directorship was good for the hospital.

Strictly speaking, 1948 and the coming of the NHS saw the end of the Hospital's responsibility and control over the ICR but a separation of their activities was neither desirable nor possible. Strong links, especially in appointments, have continued to this day. From 1948 the government stopped research funding to the Royal Marsden Hospital and insisted that all research and academic appointments be made through the ICR – effectively leaving the Hospital with only a service function. But the Hospital was not happy with this and continued to carry out and support research, especially after about 1955. It paid the salaries of some of the clinical academics and supported their clinical work, but the Institute can and does claim ownership for any research done by a Hospital academic. Most recently the Government has ordained that all nurse training and research has to be under other management. The Institute has taken it on so now nursing research and training, which was the Hospital's special baby, can no longer be considered as a feather in its cap.

But any history of the Hospital must continue to include the activities of the ICR in so far as they impacted upon the work in the clinics. For example, during the 20 years to 1970, the much-enlarged department of chemistry synthesized many potential anticancer agents and three were, by the standards of the day, highly successful. They were busulphan, chlorambucil and melphalan – all still in use today. It was the close association of the ICR/RMH complex which allowed the whole process of synthesis, animal testing and human clinical trial to go so smoothly. Later it was Haddow who encouraged Dr Wiltshaw to try out the new platinum-based compound, cisplatin, despite the fact that it appeared to act in a similar way to many previously produced drugs. It turned out to be very active against many human tumours and now it, together with its sister compound, carboplatin, are probably the most widely used anticancer agents in the world. Carboplatin was developed at the ICR on the basis that it would avoid most of the serious toxicities of cisplatin without reducing efficacy, and so it has turned out. For about the past ten years the emphasis of the ICR has moved away from chemical synthesis towards the search for particular genes associated with various malignancies, and more recently gene manipulation for therapeutic purposes. The first clinical trial of gene therapy began in 1995.

While these subjects have been the main areas of interest to the Hospital it must be understood that the Institute of Cancer Research is involved in many other fields, including epidemiology, viruses and basic problems of normal and abnormal growth. It has major departments devoted to leukaemia research and all aspects of breast cancer. The first is supported by the Leukaemia Research Fund and is headed by Professor M Greaves and the second by a variety of granting bodies. Special laboratories are presently being built at the London site by the charity Breakthrough to bring together all those in the Hospital and Institute involved in trying to finally overcome breast cancer.

Chapter 7

PROGRESS IN RADIOTHERAPY AND PHYSICS

The Cancer Hospital was one of the first to recognize the therapeutic possibilities of X-rays in the treatment of malignant disease. The first X-ray therapies were given in 1903 when a special department was established in the charge of a Dr Pollock. The apparatus and radium were in the care of a Mr Westlake (1884–1927). This unusual man had been chief dispenser/pharmacist at the Hospital for many years and is credited with laying the technical foundations of radiotherapy in Britain. He became the first secretary and was a founder member of the Society of Radiographers. When the Hospital built the Research Institute in 1911 the new electrical laboratories included were said to be 'a model of what a Roentgen laboratory should be'. By this time a Dr R Knox was in charge of the department (1910–1928) and following co-operation with Siemen Brothers in terms of equipment and layout, produced perhaps the first department to be designed professionally. The other member of the team was an X-ray physicist called C E S Phillips, who was employed on a part-time basis.

Dr Woodburn-Morrison became Head of department in 1929 after Knox's death and within a year the University of London had recognized the value of the group and its innovative work by granting him the first University of London Chair in Radiology. Earlier the University had recommended that physics be strengthened and by 1931 a new electrical department was ready in the main hospital building. It was staffed by six full-time staff including physicists, one of whom was Val Mayneord (1927–1964) whose contribution to medical physics and to the Cancer Hospital was to prove of crucial importance.

One of Mayneord's earliest collaborations was with Ernest Kennaway on the fluorescence excited by UV light of the fractions of the coal tar carcinogens being investigated at the Cancer Institute using spectroscopy. He made the fundamental observation that the same characteristic spectroscopic bands were to be found in spectra of tars and other carcinogenic substances. It was for this work that he received the first Anna Fuller Prize (USA) in 1939, together with Kennaway and Heiger.

Figure 7.1 Professor Val Mayneord FRS

Mayneord worked in close proximity to the medical staff who were delivering X-ray therapy and diagnostic radiology, so he quickly turned his attention to developing an ionization method for measuring X-ray doses. The internationally agreed definition of the 'roentgen' as a unit of X-ray measurement was established in 1928, but before that Mayneord had set up a parallel-plate ionization chamber and had evaluated the pastille dose in an absolute unit – effectively in roentgens. The pastille dose was based on the change of colour induced by X-rays in a pastille of barium platinocyanide and remained in use for many years. Mayneord then turned his attention to the problem of absorption of energy by soft tissues and to what was called secondary electron emissions from metal foils and animal tissues, including bone. By 1932 his researches were gaining acceptance among radiotherapists and his first book, *The Physics of X-ray Therapy* was published in 1929. It was a landmark in X-ray literature and was said to have helped to establish a new era in quantitative X-ray therapy. Mayneord also showed that in order to improve therapeutic effectiveness of X-ray machines voltages would have to increase to the megavoltage level rather than the smaller incremental increases proposed above the 400Kv apparatus available in the 1930s.

Mayneord also worked on the measurement of radiation doses from radium and from radium sources of various shapes. He was able to plot three-dimensional dose distributions using a dose contour projector, which he invented himself. This could be used for both radium and X-ray sources and represented a marked step forward in clinical dosimetry. Further research on dose of irradiation and human tissue absorption led Mayneord to the definition of an 'integral dose', defined as integral of dose times mass over the mass of tissue irradiated by a beam. It was therefore a measure of the total energy absorbed by the tissue and its unit was called the 'gram-roentgen'. Later he generalized the concept of a reciprocal relation between radiation source and absorber as the reciprocity theorem, and used it in determining dose at the points distant from similar radium configurations. The same ideas were later used to calculate doses within the body when using gamma-emitting radionuclides.

The first Chair of Physics as applied to medicine was given to Mayneord by the University of London in 1940. No one was more deserving. He had a strong team at the Cancer Hospital and a world-wide reputation so it was not surprising that after the war the Government asked him to go to Canada for a year as consultant in connection with radiobiological aspects of atomic energy. When he returned he wanted to widen the scope of his department to investigate the application of radioactive isotopes for therapy and diagnosis and to tackle the problems of radiation protection. For this he needed a far larger department and special facilities, so he and David Smithers sought considerable enlargement of hospital premises in London. When that was denied by the Government the expansion had to be sited in Sutton.

By this time Val Mayneord had a group of six assistant physicists and numbers were swelled by PhD students and visiting scientists. The new premises in Sutton were in use in 1958 but only in 1963 were the modern X-ray therapy machines in use, housed close to the physics department. Smithers then took his team and many of his patients to Sutton. Nuclear medicine was in its infancy when Mayneord's group produced the first scanner for making the distribution of an isotope visible in the body. Despite some scepticism among other professionals it was in use for about a decade.

Mayneord was appointed as chairman or member of many national and international committees on radiation hazards. His department looked at alpha radioactivity in nature, especially foodstuffs, and he and his colleagues devised sensitive equipment to measure very low levels of activity. One bizarre finding was that the brazil nut was one of the most radioactive foods, with activity 30 times higher than its nearest rival. A comprehensive system of badges to measure radiation received by staff in their hospital work was set up and received

Figure 7.2 Professor Sir David Smithers

doses were regularly recorded. Val Mayneord also investigated the mechanism of radiation carcinogenesis over many years, culminating in his last book *Carcinogenesis and Radiation Risk: A Biomathematical Reconnaissance.*

Although Mayneord was the major intellect in physics he could not accomplish all this alone. He had many distinguished colleagues, including Len Lamerton (1938–1980) who began radiobiological studies just after the war and became Professor in biophysics in 1960. Later he was Dean and Director at the Institute. Others of note are J E Roberts, Joan Honeyburne, J R Clarkson and later N G Trott. He was lucky to have a fine instrument maker in H C Hodt, who built many of the machines required in-house where there was an excellent workshop, later enlarged in Sutton by Mr Hodt. Mayneord won many prizes and was elected a Fellow of the Royal Society in 1965. He also became a Commander of the Order of the British Empire in 1957, but despite all the accolades he remained a considerate and charming man who retained a loyal and grateful staff over the long period of his directorship. He retired in 1964 and died in 1988 but his department continues to thrive and remains one of the leading centres of medical physics in Europe.

While the physicists gained from a close association with the radiotherapists the doctors also benefited greatly from the innovative work and intellectual stimulation of Mayneord and his staff. Two important hospital appointments were made in 1937 when David Smithers and Emmanuel Lederman joined Professor Woodburn-Morrison. Both were to enhance the reputation of radiotherapy at the Royal Marsden Hospital. Shortly after their arrival the Professor had to resign because of ill health. He was replaced by Dr Flood who was away in the army for the duration of the second world war. Smithers was made Acting Director and Lederman headed the radium department. Both men were young, ambitious and dynamic but had very different characters and qualities. They soon became rivals and this lead to friction which developed into an active dislike between them. Smithers (1937–1973) was a talented physician with excellent patient rapport. He was also a good teacher but his main strengths were good organizational skills and political acumen, which he may have learned from his father, who was an active Member of Parliament.

It was not long before Smithers began to try to reorganize the Hospital by writing a series of memoranda to the Board and others, often promoting ideas which were somewhat revolutionary at the time. One of the earliest, dated January 1943, was headed: 'Suggested Reorganisation of the Royal Cancer Hospital' was partly a response to the Cancer Bill of 1938, which asked local authorities to plan services for cancer care in about 30 different sites in the London area. Smithers suggested only six sites to cover the whole of London, the Home Counties and Sussex, each equipped to treat approximately 1000 new patients a year with radiotherapy. The paper also recognized that surgical expertise was more difficult to organize. It notes: 'The disasters due to bad radiotherapy, whether those of overtreatment and necrosis or inadequate treatment and failure, have stressed the necessity for sending patients to an efficient department. That the same consideration should apply to the surgical treatment of cancer is not yet so generally accepted however obvious it may appear to those who see some of the results of surgery carried out in small hospitals all over the country.' These ideas were radical and some were disregarded until recently when the Calman Report on cancer services (1995) was implemented and cancer services were concentrated in recognized cancer units and cancer centres. Within the Cancer Hospital itself Smithers wanted separation of radiology from radium and X-ray therapy and equal rank and recognition of status between surgeons and radiotherapists. He recommended the appointment of visiting surgical specialists to have regular joint clinics with radiotherapists, especially for gynaecological and head and neck cancers. Smithers also recommended a reorganization of hospital records to enable statistical analysis to measure outcomes. These suggestions were gradually implemented and by 1945 eight other hospitals were co-operating in joint clinics to decide on the management of new cases and the follow-up of old ones.

In 1954 Smithers started to plan a cancer registry. He wanted the Hospital to establish and endow a cancer registry with the object of 'providing a service and an opportunity for clinical cancer research throughout the hospitals in south east England'. Although a registry was set up it was very labour-intensive and lay people visited hospitals to try to extract data from hospital notes where frequently the information was either not available or was recorded in a manner only intelligible to someone with medical knowledge. The result was that the registry data were frequently inaccurate and the lack of computing power, which came much later, made analysis cumbersome and often superficial. Nevertheless the registry has survived and now covers most of the hospitals in south east England although the RMH no longer runs it.

After the war Smithers joined forces with Val Mayneord to set up a department of nuclear physics as applied to medicine which would have a national impact. The plan was agreed with the Ministry of Health in 1947 and a building was well under way by 1956. In the event the importance of radioactive isotopes to medicine was not as great as they had expected and the emphasis on nuclear medicine and radiotherapy began to shift towards the use of drugs, so that as the Sutton site developed Smithers decided that it should be a complete hospital, with a strong clinical research component. At the same time he thought the London site should be for surgical and out-patient services only. This was unrealistic and was resisted by the Board, but since Smithers was a powerful member of that body, having been on it continuously since 1948, he was able to steer a great deal of money and other resources in the direction of Sutton, where he was king. This led to friction between colleagues who were devoting their efforts to one site only.

Smithers was made Director of the radiotherapy and radium departments in 1944 and gained the Chair in radiotherapy in 1948. He was knighted 21 years later for his services to medicine. Over the later years of his working life he concentrated on two things: first, the development of Sutton as a first-class clinical research centre and second, to confine his clinical work to the management of lymphoma, including Hodgkin's disease and testicular tumours. His choice was fortunate, for both these tumour types were beginning to benefit remarkably from a combined attack using radiotherapy and chemotherapy. Smithers had brought Gordon Hamilton-Fairley to Sutton to help on the medical side and after his death Smithers collaborated with Tim McElwain. He was also responsible for setting up a multidisciplinary team, including data managers, to conduct and properly record studies, although, unfortunately he did not take the opportunity to undertake randomized trials.

Smithers and Alex Haddow, the Director of the Institute, did not get on. Smithers felt that the Institute was wrong to concentrate so much of its efforts on new cytotoxic drugs and he wanted closer collaboration between scientists and doctors to answer questions raised in the clinic. In 1969 he wrote yet another memorandum attacking what he called old-fashioned ideas that the final solution to cancer would be found at the molecular level. He wanted a clinician to head the Institute (perhaps he had himself in mind) and a joint Board for the ICR and RMH. The latter was not possible because of the independence of the ICR and the fact that the Hospital was owned and funded by the Government, but this was clearly a direct attack on Alex Haddow. On this occasion nothing came of Smithers' recommendations.

Mannie Lederman (1937–1976) was appointed at the same time as Smithers but he was a very different character with talents that complemented Smithers'. He was an innovative physician and used the advantages available in the physics department to great effect, but he was no match for Smithers in organization and medical politics. He always appeared to come second to the professor, increasingly seeming to hide away doing his own thing in the basement area, which was still known as the radium department long after a separate practising department ceased to exist. Lederman concentrated on gathering a large practice dealing with some of the rarer tumours including head and neck, eye and gynaecological lesions. There is no doubt that the garnering of these practices was facilitated by the collaboration with other hospitals set up by Smithers but they flourished because of the flare and dedication shown by Lederman himself. He and Mayneord worked together on the difficult area of dose distribution of radiation in the special circumstances of the head and neck.

They also sought to solve the problem of damage to the eye, especially the lens, during treatment of orbital tumours. It is to Lederman's and the Marsden's credit that of 30 original papers picked out for special mention in *Modern Radiation Oncology* published in 1978 three were reproduced from his department. They described the management of cancers of the larynx, orbit, and one by his colleague and protégé Vera Dalley on the hypopharynx. All were considered classics of their time and sit cheek by jowl with papers by such giants as Gilbert Fletcher (USA), Vera Peters (Canada), Henry Kaplan (USA) and a medical oncologist, Sidney Farber (USA). These and many other papers earned Lederman a well-deserved international reputation but he seems always to have felt himself to be in Smithers' shadow, despite the fact that Smithers produced little in the way of published clinical research. Lederman was an especially good teacher of post-graduate students and many radiotherapists around the world admit their debt to him. His lectures were vivid and memorable and were often given without a script. He was a generous collaborator with surgeons and physicians inside and outside the RMH, an attribute not always evident in David Smithers.

In 1958 Julian Bloom (1958–1987) joined the department. Having been at the Middlesex Hospital for some time he had already made a name for himself with a study of breast cancer survival in relation to histopathological tumour characteristics. When he joined the Cancer Hospital, subspecialization of radiotherapy work meant that this practice was already catered for. However he took on two difficult areas of work: tumours of the nervous system and urological tumours. He too had a seminal paper reprinted in *Modern Radiation Oncology,* his subject being treatment and prognosis in medulloblastoma. It was originally published in 1967 and was a study of 82 children under the age of 15. Bloom showed that cure was possible with radiotherapy provided that sufficient doses were applied. He worked closely with Institute scientists and oversaw experimental animal work there. Out of this he concluded that progesterone might be of value in cancer of the kidney. His initial human studies suggested that tumour progression might be halted, and in some cases reversed. Although it turned out later that the beneficial effects of progesterone were minimal it was a very interesting concept. Later Bloom concentrated more on collaborative studies on a multimodel therapy of bladder cancer. He, together

Figure 7.3 Dr Julian Bloom

with his surgical colleague David Wallace, set up the Co-operative Urological Cancer Group in the south east. The group conducted perhaps the earliest bladder cancer randomized trials using surgery, radiotherapy and chemotherapy. He laid the foundations for a special brain tumour unit at the RMH by working with surgeons at Atkinson Morley, the Hospital for Sick Children and the National Hospital for Nervous Diseases. He retired in 1987 and died only two years later.

These three, Smithers, Lederman and Bloom, were the big names of radiotherapy. The department they left was and is one of the strongest and largest in the country. It has a good training programme for physicians and radiographers and continues to benefit from the work of physics. However, in recent

Figure 7.4 Professor Sir Michael Peckham

years the radiotherapists have recognized the increasing importance of drug treatment and Smither's successors Michael Peckham, and latterly Alan Horwich, have had an increasing interest in chemotherapy studies, sometimes in preference to radiotherapy, their own subject.

Michael Peckham became professor in 1973 at a very early age, and he inherited Smithers' large practice of testicular tumours and lymphoma cases after only three years as a senior lecturer and honorary consultant at the Royal Marsden Hospital. Peckham classified testicular cancer on the basis of the sites and bulk of tumour found following extensive investigation, including lymphography. This classification, later known as the Marsden system, enabled outcomes in similar cases to be compared across the world literature and was used in many centres. He also worked with Tim McElwain on the treatment of Hodgkin's disease, using a combination of drugs where chlorambucil was used instead of the older, more toxic, nitrogen mustard introduced by the National Cancer Institute. Their studies showed that the less toxic regimen using chlorambucil was equally effective and had fewer side-effects – especially less nausea and vomiting. Peckham organized many international meetings, giving the Hospital excellent publicity. He resigned in 1986 to become the Director of the Post-graduate Medical Federation and in 1990 was appointed by the Government to be the first Director of Research and Development at the Department of Health. He was knighted for his work when he completed his five-year contract.

Alan Horwich now holds the Chair and is Dean at the Institute as well as Director of Clinical Research at the RMH. He has 12 consultant or senior lecturers and support from physics which now boasts a scientific staff of more than 50. Apart from carrying out research the physics staff are involved with radiotherapy machinery, radioisotopes – both diagnostic and therapeutic – ultrasound, magnetic resonance imaging and spectroscopy, and radiation protection, probably the largest department in the organization.

Chapter 8

THE MEDICAL TREATMENT OF CANCER

From the early days of its existence the Cancer Hospital tested new compounds which were considered to have potential benefits for cancer patients. This fitted well with Marsden's philosophy and those of his surgical colleagues when, in the Annual Report of 1854, they described cancer as a constitutional disease. William Marsden repeatedly stressed the importance of treating the whole person and while he was totally opposed to quack medicine being used in the Hospital he was not against innovation. Many reports record the use of new substances having undergone testing in hospital patients, presumably overseen by surgeons, and the remedies were all found to be useless. The details of these studies were either not recorded or were lost, but it is probable that any medical remedy was given for end-stage disease when even holy water would prove wanting.

The first serious attempt at medical treatment was a study of a vaccine prepared from micrococcus neoformans. Nineteen beds were allocated to Dr Horder, the first hospital physician, for a clinical trial in 1909–10. Again the therapy was a failure.

In 1935 when Kennaway, as Director of the Institute, was continuing his studies on carcinogenic compounds he began a collaboration with Alexander Haddow on the use of high doses of certain hydrocarbons to slow growth. It was natural that the emphasis on carcinogenic effects should be coupled with studies of cell proliferation and its control, and Haddow was particularly interested in growth inhibitory substances. Haddow joined the Institute staff in 1937 and embarked on a search for water soluble cancer inhibitory substances. The Research Institute Annual Report of 1940 states: 'This work on chemotherapy has reached a stage when careful clinical trial might give valuable results.' Two years later a Dr Watkinson was appointed 'to oversee clinical trials of anti-cancer drugs' produced in the Chester Beatty building and manufactured in collaboration with Imperial Chemical Industries. Although it was a good time for the Hospital to facilitate the use of anti-cancer drugs it did not seem to be overly enthusiastic and when Haddow and his team began to use urethane they had to seek the help of several other hospitals as well as the Marsden to acquire enough patients. The paper on urethane was written with Dr Edith Paterson of the Christie Hospital, Manchester, where many of the cases were treated, and published in 1946. Forty-five patients with leukaemia were treated over three years but the details show that the total white cell counts were high and the spleens grossly enlarged, pointing to the advanced stage of disease when treatment was attempted. Nevertheless transient responses were observed. Urethane (ethyl carbamate) was one of the phenyl urethanes which inhibited growth in plants, in spontaneous mammary cancer in the mouse and in the implanted Walker rat carcinoma. It is an interesting compound but its effects on animals were found to persist only while the compound was being given. It also had a profound histological effect on animal tumours resulting in an overgrowth of stroma, perhaps due to differentiation of the malignant cells (Haddow, 1947). It may have been a pity that it arrived on the scene so early for today's testing of such a compound would have been much more thorough and one wonders if a really useful agent has been missed.

At about this time the Institute and Hospital set up a Clinical Research Committee with representatives from the Institute, including the Director. The Hospital was represented by physicians, the Professor of radiotherapy and surgeons. This committee was, according to David Galton, an extremely responsible body which carefully considered the justification for clinical trial of specific agents. Most interestingly, the ethical implications of trials of completely new drugs were taken very seriously. These issues were rarely, if ever, discussed in a formal way in other hospitals at that time even in the USA.

Galton was appointed at the Institute in 1947 to undertake the investigation of new drugs in the clinical setting. He had to report on the progress of any trial to the Committee every month and had great respect for their deliberations and conclusions. However, the strict controls the Committee imposed resulted again in the failure to use chemotherapy early enough to give the drugs a chance to show their real worth. This became obvious when Wayne Rundles used urethane for myeloma in the USA much earlier than Galton would have been allowed to do, thereby producing greater benefit. Galton was instructed by the Committee that the patient must be told that no orthodox treatment was available to him before offering a new drug, that the drug had never been used before but

Figure 8.1 Dr David Galton CBE

that there was reason to believe that it might help, although at the doses given to minimize toxicity it was very unlikely that he would benefit personally. Despite all these stringent conditions and the fact that few had been told explicitly that they had cancer, Galton could not recall any patient refusing a trial drug.

It is important here to explain how drugs were tested on animals at the Institute, not only for their anti-cancer effects but also for toxicity. Drugs were chosen for their growth inhibiting characteristics and the Walker rat tumour was selected as the chief test system. This tumour came from a patient originally but had been passed through many animal generations. It grew quickly and at a uniform rate, so that retardation of growth could be seen within a short space of time, but unfortunately it bore little resemblance to any tumour in man. After dosing the rats with the test compound growth retardation of the implanted tumours was measured daily and the results compared with control untreated animals. Tests for toxicity included measurement of growth retardation in baby animals, weight loss in adults. Studies on mutagenicity and carcinogenic testing as well as cytogenetic damage were all routine. But it was the studies of immediate toxicity, especially to bone marrow function, which led to scientific error. Experiments had to be completed quickly because of space restrictions in the animal house. All the growth inhibiting substances showed their effects within a short space of time and the practice of killing test animals after 72 hours observation became established. All went well until the drug busulphan (Myleran) came under scrutiny. First, this was highly effective against the test tumour; second, the routine bone marrow examination 24-hours after dosing, unlike other growth inhibitors, showed no damage to that tissue, so it was thought not to be toxic. However, early clinical trials and longer-term observation of other animals showed a novel type of damage which did not become obvious in the bone marrow until 14 days after treatment. This compound was killing the stem cells of the marrow and the major effect on the blood cells was seen only six weeks later in humans. The other problem was that by choosing a rapidly growing tumour to select possibly useful drugs the Institute was selecting agents to stop rapid growth rather than malignant growth. This error was repeated in all other institutes, and later Haddow was to be amazed how much the resulting anti-cancer drugs could and did achieve.

When David Galton arrived at the Institute he had little to offer patients apart from the new agents being produced there. There were really only four compounds which had been developed elsewhere, with urethane and busulphan developed locally. Stilboestrol was producing limited benefit in cancer of the prostate and breast. Nitrogen mustard (code name HN2) had been produced following the investigation of the effects of mustard gas on the bone marrow, lymphoid system and gastrointestinal tract. This highly toxic compound was given to Goodman and Gilman in the USA to investigate its possible usefulness in man. They tested it on patients with lymphoma, producing dramatic results in some cases. The results were published in 1946. Also in 1946 Sidney Farber published his first paper on the use of anti-folates at the children's hospital in Boston (Aminopterin and later Amethopterin) in acute lymphoblastic leukaemia. Again short-lived remissions were produced. Adrenocorticotropic hormones were being produced which did have value in the management of some malignancies, in particular the lymphomas and chronic lymphocytic leukaemia.

Busulphan, synthesized by Timmis at the ICR, was the first useful drug for chronic myeloid leukaemia, although it did produce regressions in other tumours including, occasionally, breast cancer. It had the advantages of being given by mouth, causing no immediate side effects and, at first, it's only toxicity seemed to be bone marrow suppression. Galton and some of his haematological friends came together under the auspices of the Medical Research Council (MRC) to conduct a randomized study comparing the results of treatment with busulphan with radiotherapy to the spleen. Patients were accrued from 1959–1967 and showed that the drug was just as effective as radiotherapy in controlling the disease, and was even of benefit when radiation stopped being useful – although the opposite was not the case. Unfortunately neither treatment was curative, but the principles of randomized trials for malignant disease by the MRC including a strong statistical input had been established.

The clinical arm of the Institute was allowed to operate within the small department of medicine at the Hospital but as with early radiotherapy the new discipline had to work under the authority of others. Galton had no clinics or admitting rights of his own nor was he a member of the medical committee. This state of affairs continued until 1964 when he was granted NHS consultant sessions. The embryonic medical oncology unit was housed in a couple of rooms in a cottage acquired by the Hospital across the road from the main building in Dovehouse Street. Staff, usually one assistant to Galton and a postgraduate fellow, would attend clinics run by general physicians and also attended by a radiotherapist. Discussions about whether drugs or radiation were appropriate in specific cases were often heated, but it slowly became accepted that in the case of leukaemia and generalised lymphoma local radiotherapy was of less value to patients than the use of drugs. The unit had no laboratory facility of its own but worked with Elson, and later Tom Connors at the ICR, on the effects of drugs on animals.

The medical climate obtaining when Galton first joined the Cancer Hospital was sceptical about cancer medicine. In teaching hospitals cancer was taught by surgeons, and more systematically by pathologists, but radiotherapists who were now the major treaters of malignant disease rarely took part in undergraduate teaching. At the same time most patients who were beyond the help of surgery, either because of large local disease or metastatic growth, were referred to radiotherapists or were sent home to die. One might have expected radiotherapists to be sympathetic to efforts to try out drugs where radiotherapy had failed but most greeted the advent of chemotherapy with scepticism or even hostility.

Without the support of junior staff Galton had to administer his own blood transfusions, which were major time-wasters. Blood and fluids came in glass bottles and needles had to be sharpened and sterilized for reuse. There was no fresh blood or blood fractions to support patients when blood counts were low, which was a frequent problem in a population where repeated courses of radiotherapy to be followed by a cytotoxic drug had depleted marrow reserves. Giving intravenous drugs via infusion systems where the needles were of relatively large bore so that only the larger veins could be entered was also a crude business. Venous inflammation was common, especially with the more vesicant drugs such as HN2. The only means of controlling the rate of flow of an infusion was a crude clip on rubber tubing and drugs had to be made up at the bedside. Antibiotics were in their infancy so infections in marrow-suppressed patients were very dangerous and often caused premature death. Despite all these difficulties Galton managed a good deal on his own. He wrote an article on androgen therapy in advanced breast cancer in 1950 and followed this with a review article with Smithers and others in 1952 on all aspects of breast cancer, including the value of hormonal manipulation. However because of the relative sensitivity of the haematological malignancies and Hodgkin's disease to the available drugs this dominated the practice he built up over the next few years.

After busulphan the next useful drug to come out of the Institute was chlorambucil, an oral alkylating agent synthesized by Ross. Its first clinical trial at the RMH was conducted by Galton and Till. It proved useful in lymphocytic leukaemia, Hodgkin's disease, lymphoma and ovarian carcinoma, and continues to be used for the more low-grade lymphomas and leukaemia.

Chlorambucil production at the ICR was rapidly followed by the synthesis of another alkylating agent, melphalan, by Stock and Bergel. Unfortunately it again showed a similar spectrum

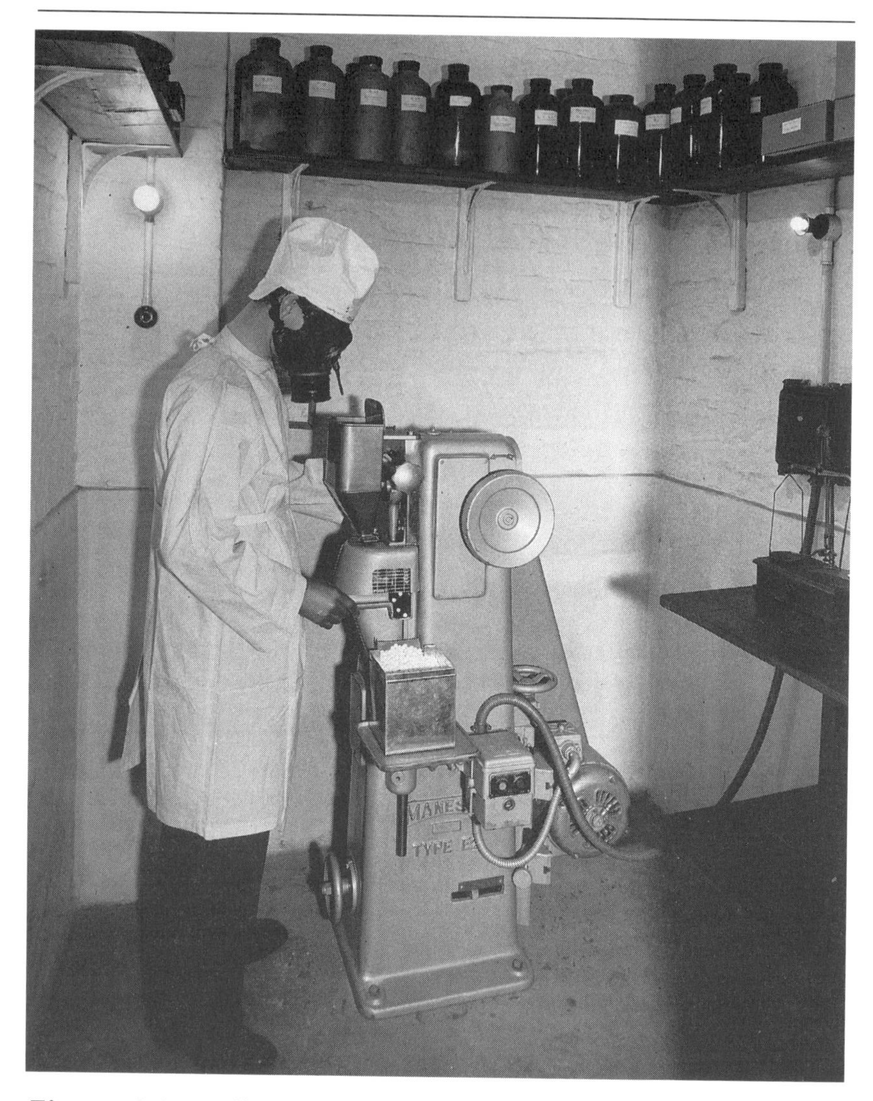

Figure 8.2 A pill-making machine used in the pharmacy to turn drugs produced in the Institute into tablets for human consumption. A second world war gas mask was worn to protect the operator from dust or vapour which might come from the compound

of action to chlorambucil and while still in use it has few advantages over the earlier compound.

By 1960 Galton had become a well-known name in international haematological circles and many postgraduate students came from abroad to work with him for 6–12 month periods, including some from Canada, USA, the USSR and Australia. However when UK postgraduates asked to study with him Galton was reluctant to take them on because there was no career path for cancer physicians in this country. Indeed what chemotherapy was given was, and still is, administered by radiotherapists.

David Galton was a man of wide biological knowledge and a gifted observer of nature. Thus his papers on new drugs and their effects were meticulous and detailed and only rarely did later studies reveal effects not noted previously by him. He was widely respected outside his own hospital but seems to have been undervalued by his local clinical colleagues. His resources remained inadequate and his staff tiny. Perhaps his quiet and modest manner and his lack of entrepreneurial skills had something to do with his inability to promote his own department and his own speciality. A rival group was set up when the Hospital formed the Clinical Research Department in 1962 under Hancock, a general physician, rather than Galton. Later this led to another group in the new Sutton site taking on bone marrow transplantation work under the haematologist Humphrey Kay. At the time Kay had no clinical experience, being a laboratory-trained doctor, but he later went on to co-ordinate and run many MRC trials in acute lymphoblastic leukaemia and set up the reverse barrier nursing ward at Sutton – the first of its kind in Europe.

The status of medical oncology was greatly enhanced when in 1968 Professor Gordon Hamilton-Fairley joined David Smithers in Sutton to run a new unit exploring immunotherapy in malignant disease, in association with Professor Peter Alexander of the ICR. Later it became an area of drug therapy when immunological manipulation failed to live up to expectations. Hamilton-Fairley was personable, able, and had political flair. He was the first Professor of Medical Oncology in the UK and trained many in the subject at his home base, St. Bartholomew's Hospital. Had he lived longer cancer medicine would undoubtedly have grown more rapidly in the UK but in

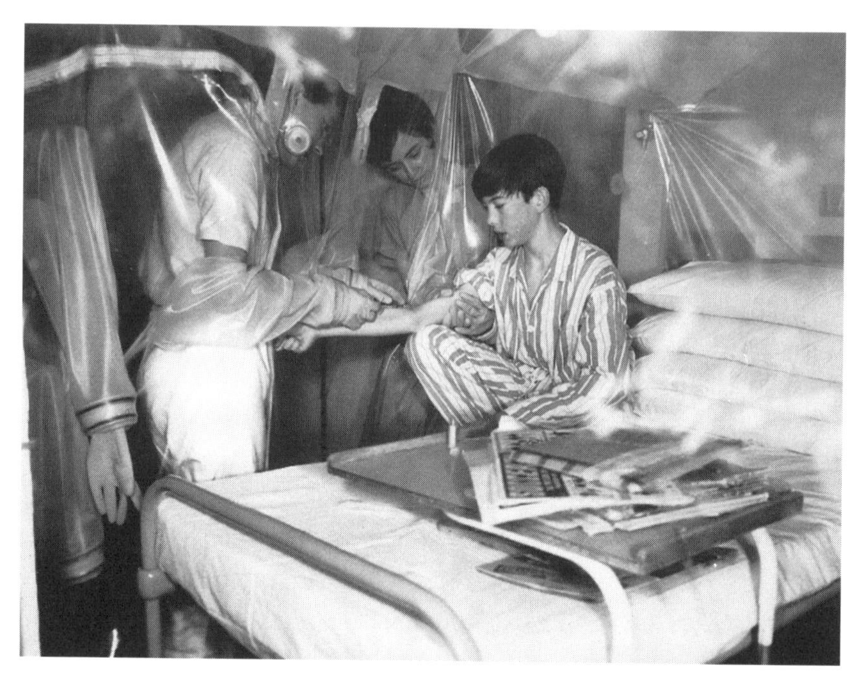

Figure 8.3 A boy being treated through the plastic sheeting of the earliest attempts at reverse barrier nursing in 1973 when bone marrow transplantation was started for cases of acute leukaemia

1975 he was killed by a bomb placed under a car by the Irish Republican Army. The bomb was meant for someone else but exploded while Gordon was out in the street. He was only 45. His relationship with the RMH was wholly beneficial.

The reverse barrier nursing ward was built at Sutton to allow high doses of drugs to be given to patients with a view to eradicating the leukaemia. This required the transplantation of donor bone marrow to replace the destroyed leukaemic tissue. At first transplantation work was a rather hit-and-miss affair with many serious complications, but after the advent of tissue compatibility testing and the use of appropriate donors Ray Powles, who took over from Kay, was able to produce successful transplants on a regular basis. The first successful transplant took place in 1973 and the patient is alive and well today. Now the method is routine but Ray Powles is in the forefront of continual refinement of method and reducing the toxicity and hazards of the procedure.

Between 1950 and 1970 Galton's group extended their work to childhood tumours, testicular and ovarian cancer, and continued work on the use of antioestrogens for breast cancer. This was a period of rapid growth of new and useful drugs such as the vinca alkaloids, (vinblastine and vincristine) the anti cancer antibiotics (bleomycin and rubidomycin) and cyclophosphamide, 6-mercaptopurine and asparaginase. Most of the new drugs were developed elsewhere and the ICR began to scale down its programme for producing drugs from scratch as costs rose and it became clear that only the drug companies had the necessary resources to do this successfully. Nevertheless, Galton's group was able to test out all these agents at an early stage because of its international reputation. On one occasion the group was sent a small supply of vinblastine from Canada and a vial went missing in the Hospital so a telephone call was made for more drug. The Canadians were horrified that the RMH had been so careless with a drug which at that time was estimated to cost 10,000 dollars to produce.

In 1972 David Galton resigned, to spend the rest of his working life at the Royal Postgraduate Hospital in Hammersmith. There he could concentrate on haematological malignancies and work with his long-term friend Professor John Dacie. Later Galton was given a personal Chair by the London University and a CBE for his contribution to medicine. He hoped that his assistant would step into his shoes but Marsden and ICR politics are never as simple as that.

A tremendous boost was given to medical oncologists, as they are now called, when a combination of drugs known by the acronym MOPP was shown by De Vita and colleagues to produce long-term remissions in Hodgkin's disease in approximately 80% of previously untreated cases, and possible cures seemed likely (1970).

Although the Royal Marsden Hospital had discussed the formation of an academic department of medicine as early as

1956 and a first attempt was made in 1962 under Dr Thompson Hancock, it was not until 1972 that the first professor was appointed during the Directorship at the ICR of Professor Symington. Symington believed that science-trained clinicians could improve the links between the Institute and Hospital but this was not entirely successful under the first professor, Phil Bondy (1972–1977) who came from Yale and had little knowledge of cancer or of the workings of the NHS. In any event the close relationship between the ICR and RMH is more dependent on the relevance of ICR work to the diagnosis and management of cancer in man than it is to individual personalities.

Tim McElwain (1972–1990), who had been working under Hamilton-Fairley, was made senior lecturer and honorary consultant in 1972. This was a popular choice for Sutton. His postgraduate training was at St. Bartholomew's, the Royal Postgraduate Hospital and the Hospital for Sick Children. He already had experience in cancer work, particularly childhood malignancies. Mac, as he was generally known, took up the cause of proper recognition for cancer physicians. Cancer was still a tiny subspeciality, with doctors' salaries mainly funded by cancer charities rather than the NHS. With others he formed the Association of Cancer Physicians and was later its president. This organization has played a major role in getting more physicians into NHS posts and acquiring respectability for cancer medicine within the Royal College of Physicians. Mac was first and foremost a clinician and teacher of the first order but he had no formal research training or experience. However he saw the need to modify and improve the sometimes highly toxic combination chemotherapy which was now coming into fashion. He tried to reduce the side-effects and toxicities of the MOPP regimen for Hodgkin's disease (the letters stand for Mustard (HN2), vincristine (Oncovin) procarbazine and prednisolone). The most unpleasant of these drugs was HN2, which caused severe nausea and vomiting and frequent venous inflammation at the site of injection. Vincristine also had a tendency to produce peripheral neuropathy, sometimes leading to

Figure 8.4 Professor Timothy McElwain

partial paralysis of the wrist and foot. By changing the regimen replacing HN2 with chlorambucil and vincristine with vinblastine Mac produced a more acceptable therapy with no loss of efficacy. This regimen, known as ChlVVP, allowed most patients to have their treatment as out-patients rather than having to stay overnight once a month during the six month course, as happened with MOPP. Mac also tested many drugs for their potential to reduce nausea and vomiting. He supported multiple drug treatment for acute leukaemia and wrote an article on the subject in the *British Medical Journal* as early as 1969. Mac worked with Smithers, and later with Peckham, in a multispecialty testicular tumour unit at Sutton. The unit was rather slow at taking up the curative combination regimen of cisplatin, vinblastine and bleomycin (PVB) pioneered by Einhorn in the USA, but when they did take it on Mac set about trying to improve it. He introduced a less toxic combination of cisplatin, etoposide and bleomycin (BEP). Later modification by Horwich replacing cisplatin by carboplatin again improved therapeutic acceptability. The patients' interests were always uppermost in Mac's mind and this was made abundantly clear by his teaching and his support for BACUP (the British Association of Cancer United Patients) which was started by a patient to inform patients and the general public of the facts about cancer and its management. Mac joined the BACUP board and continued to work for the organization until his death.

Ten years after becoming a consultant and six years after Professor Bondy resigned McElwain was appointed to the Chair of Medicine at the ICR which was now supported financially by the Cancer Research Campaign (1982). He built up an experimental group under the leadership of John Miller at the ICR. This group was soon to show that a small priming dose of cyclophosphamide could protect the bone marrow and bowel from the worst effects of a later very large dose of melphalan, provided that the timing was right. This finding was successfully translated to man in attempts to produce meaningful regressions of metastatic melanoma. However even very high doses of melphalan only produced rather transient regressions. Mac then applied the same principles in a more sensitive tumour – namely myeloma. A small dose of cyclophosphamide was followed a few days later by removal of the patient's own bone marrow, then high dose melphalan was given immediately before the patient's extracted marrow was returned to him. Provided that the patient was not suffering from significant kidney damage due to disease, Mac was able to show that complete response rates were increased from 10–15% up to 50% with this regimen. Later he added alpha-interferon to the programme to prolong the length of these remissions.

By the time Tim McElwain became professor, Ray and Trevor Powles were already working in Sutton as senior lecturers. During his tenure Mac presided over the appointment of a consultant in palliative care, G Hanks, and another cancer physician, I Smith. Mac believed there should be no separation between NHS and ICR medical staff (town and gown, as he put it) and he managed the whole team with tact and encouragement. Many of his visitors and postgraduates were rotated through several of the medical teams and between Sutton and London. He also helped to train many consultants now running cancer services in his native New Zealand.

Bearing in mind all these good qualities it is not surprising that there was shock and distress throughout the Hospital and Institute when Mac committed suicide on 26 November 1990. Very few people knew that he had recently been severely depressed and had sought medical help but there was much speculation as to what had triggered the illness and the dreadful outcome. Tim McElwain was a perfectionist where his own standards were concerned and may have felt that the rising pressure on him to be more involved in basic science was unattainable given his lack of training in that area. There were also dramatic changes in hospital administration following the reforms of the NHS and he did not favour most of them. Finally, an article Mac wrote on survival in breast cancer had compared RMH patients and those who had gone to an alternative medicine clinic (the Bristol Clinic). The analysis showed that attendance at the Bristol Clinic did not prolong life, in fact patients died more quickly but the reason for the difference was probably the more advanced stage of the disease at presentation to the Bristol Clinic compared to the Marsden group. This flaw in the analysis of the data was not made clear in the paper and the article was rapidly and widely discussed in the press and on television, where the Bristol Clinic stoutly defended its work against what it saw as a direct attack. This study was bound to be a highly sensitive issue and it may be that Mac had not taken as much care as he should have in overseeing the wording of the article. In any event the Bristol lost many of its patients and the battle in the press became one of orthodox medicine versus alternative medicine generally. Eventually the ICR and RMH withdrew any suggestion that the Bristol Clinic's methods had played any part in the earlier demise of their patients. This very public event may have tipped over the brink a man already under severe stress. All this is conjecture and a personal view. He was much-loved and greatly valued and his place has never been filled. Not only has the Chair remained vacant, his leadership has not been replaced.

While McElwain was making his way in Sutton Eve Wiltshaw was battling alone in London. Wiltshaw had been recruited by

Figure 8.5 Dr Eve Wiltshaw OBE

Haddow as research assistant to Galton in 1957. When Galton left in 1972 she was given locum consultant sessions to run medical oncology in London. It took two years for her to be properly appointed as a consultant at the RMH after a rather unedifying wrangle between opposing senior medical staff about which of two candidates should get the job. Wiltshaw (1974–1994) had a similar training to McElwain but it was grounded in clinical haematology in America rather than paediatrics. From 1957 when she joined the ICR until her NHS appointment she was involved in the early trials of drugs with Galton and she had a wide knowledge of most cancers, including paediatric and rare tumours. By 1972 the Hospital had five cancer physicians on the staff, three at Sutton and two in London, all with growing involvement in the management of most cancers. Wiltshaw's particular interests were children's tumours, haematological malignancies, and by 1964, ovarian cancer. However with the opening of the Sutton branch Smithers took many of the lymphoma patients with him, as well as his practice in testicular cancer. When the reverse barrier nursing ward opened many of the acute leukaemia patients also went to Sutton. Later the children's ward in London was closed to concentrate the effort on one site in the purpose-built ward at Sutton. As a result Wiltshaw looked increasingly to other areas of practice and began to build a collaborative unit to manage sarcomas. Clive Harmer (radiotherapy), Alan McKinna and later Professor Westbury (surgery) and Wiltshaw began a weekly clinic which started with only 12 new cases a year and built up to more than 120 per year by 1980. Perhaps the largest practice of any hospital in the UK, it now sees about 200 new patients annually.

In 1970 Haddow called Wiltshaw to discuss a trial of a novel agent in the clinic. Haddow had become interested in the work of B Rosenberg, a physicist from the USA who had discovered in 1969 that the solution produced by the platinum electrodes in electrolysis of bacteria induced filamentous growth, that is, it inhibited cell division. Out of this observation had come much work on the action of various platinum compounds on bacteria, animal tumours and other study systems. In animals several tumour types regressed dramatically and one compound, cis platin diammine dichloride (cisplatin) was chosen for clinical trial.

In 1970 Haddow telephoned Rosenberg, at a time when few in the USA were showing any interest, to discuss Rosenberg's findings.

Haddow was given some of Rosenberg's compound and after performing some experiments on animals he was convinced that it was an important new agent. Within a year Wiltshaw was using the drug against a variety of tumours but because of her rather specialized practice several patients with very late-stage ovarian cancer were treated. These patients had relapsed, or their tumours were resistant to chlorambucil therapy. Wiltshaw recognized that the responses she observed were a great improvement on any other drug given in the same circumstances. The first clinical results were reported at the second international meeting on platinum co-ordination complexes in Oxford in 1973. Eight clinical reports were given at the meeting and only two showed exciting results: one by Higby from America reported responses in testicular cancer, and Wiltshaw's in ovarian cases. While many delegates at that meeting felt this was a very active anticancer agent most believed it was too toxic to be really useful. Wiltshaw, on the other hand, felt that much of the toxicity could be minimized by giving intravenous fluids together with the cisplatin, and by taking care to stop the drug at the first sign of neuropathy.

Wiltshaw's studies led to a valuable collaboration between the RMH and Johnson Mathey PLC, which took over the very difficult chemistry and production of cisplatin and other platinum complexes under the leadership of Dr Cleare. This company also supported the ICR when they began to look for less toxic compounds. Wiltshaw and Professor Harrap of the Institute were anxious to use a more benign compound without losing any efficacy and the collaborative effort resulted in the trial of carboplatin in 1981. This compound was selected among several possible agents because animal studies suggested that it might lack the major disadvantage of cisplatin, namely its renal toxicity. Clinical trials by Calvert, newly-appointed clinical pharmacologist at the ICR and Hospital, and Wiltshaw showed that renal toxicity had almost disappeared and the severity of nausea and vomiting had been greatly reduced. They also discovered that the neurological toxicity of cisplatin had been almost eliminated. Later a comparative trial indicated that no efficacy had been lost, although it was clear that carboplatin was more toxic to the bone marrow. In the 1990s these two compounds are the most widely used anti-cancer agents in the world and are relatively effective in a wide variety of tumour types. In 1991 the Hospital, ICR and Johnson Mathey PLC were awarded the Queen's Award for Technological Achievement for this work, the first time a hospital had been so honoured.

Wiltshaw also showed an interest in management of the Hospital and it was perhaps surprising that only two years after her consultant appointment her colleagues elected her Chairman of their Medical Committee. In 1979 she was appointed to the Board of Governors by the Secretary of State. When NHS changes brought in executive management to hospitals in the 1987 reforms Wiltshaw successfully applied for the advertised post of Director of Clinical Services (equivalent to Medical Director in other hospitals). She remained in this post until 1994 when the RMH was given Trust status and the survival of the London branch was confirmed. Her work on ovarian cancer was recognized when the Royal College of Obstetricians granted her a Fellowship *ad eundem* in 1990 and a year later she was honoured with an OBE for services to medicine, having been involved in the care of cancer patients for 39 years.

Cancer of the breast has been a major concern at the Hospital since its inception and there has always been a preponderance of such cases coming through its doors. Haddow and Galton were involved in early attempts to treat this common tumour with stilboestrol when others were using castration and androgens, all of which methods produced some dramatic regressions in particular cases. Later Boesen (a member of Galton's team) and Bloom tried out some early antioestrogenic substances, but it was not until tamoxifen was available (triphenylethylene, 1971) that effective, almost non-toxic hormone therapy could be used with consistent benefit. At about this time workers in the USA were giving a cocktail of cytotoxic drugs after surgery to women who were perceived to be at high risk of recurrence. It took several years to show that this approach improved survival, as indeed did the use of tamoxifen in similar circumstances. When both approaches were combined the survival benefit was enhanced again. The breast group at the RMH took up these therapies very early and tried out many other drugs and regimens for patients with later stage disease (T Powles and I Smith). Their greatest contribution may prove to be the prevention of the development of breast cancer in women at high risk, especially those with a strong family history of the disease. It was evident to Trevor Powles that the population of women coming to the early diagnostic clinic originally set up by Peter Greening contained a subgroup of well women who were anxious about a risk of breast cancer either because of such cancers having already occurred in their families or because of breast pathology which they felt might later show as a cancer. Powles wanted to try to prevent breast cancer developing and he chose high risk cases in this clinic for his experiment. He brought a proposal to the Hospital ethical committee and to outside bodies, including the Cancer Research Campaign (CRC), and the first randomized study began in 1986. Appropriate women attending the early diagnostic clinic were asked to agree in writing to entry into the study where half were given Tamoxifen while half received a placebo, on a daily basis for five years. Analysis of the first 200 cases showed good compliance and few side effects, but only 47% of those asked had agreed to take part. The study continued with a larger trial and by 1995 2500 women had joined, and were planned to continue treatment for 8 years. By this time considerable interest was being shown around the world, especially in the USA, and a national study was started there on the same lines as the RMH trial. Similar large scale trials were started in Italy and elsewhere in the UK. It is still not known whether tamoxifen will prevent breast cancer developing in this population, but if it does a major leap forward will have been achieved.

This study illustrates how far cancer medicine has advanced since 1947 when urethane was first tried in the dying patient. It also shows how the Royal Marsden Hospital and Institute for Cancer Research have remained in the forefront of the battle.

Chapter 9

CANCER NURSING AND NURSE TRAINING

Nurses joined the Cancer Hospital when in-patient facilities became available. The first matron, a Miss Scivier, was appointed in 1861 when the Hospital at Fulham Road was opened. This was before nursing had become a respected profession and in many hospitals the quality of nursing care was very poor. The first Institute of Nursing was established by Elizabeth Fry in 1884. The experiences of the Crimean war (1853–1856) together with the work of Florence Nightingale both during and after that war, improved the status of nurses and the quality of person entering the profession. In the Cancer Hospital quality nursing care has always been an important part of its good reputation and as early as 1873 Dr Alexander Marsden, who had been at Scutari and must have worked with Florence Nightingale, reported to the hospital committee: 'During my long hospital career I have never seen kinder or more efficient nursing, and I feel we owe much to our Nurses for the manner in which they have discharged their most arduous and responsible duties.' This is a rare accolade from a surgeon to nurses and has been well deserved of the Cancer Hospital nurses from that day to this.

The governors also valued the nurses and did everything they could to support them. At first nurses were housed on the top floor of the original building but by 1900 special accommodation was provided, separate from the main building, to house those on night duty to guarantee a quiet environment during the day. Three years later it was necessary to provide more rooms so a new building was erected containing 25 rooms, two sitting rooms and the 'usual offices'. The venture cost £5,000 and further money was spent on a tennis court in 1929. Nursing numbers increased rapidly and by 1910 it was necessary to build a whole wing, now known as Mulberry House, for their accommodation. Much later when staff preferred to live away from the campus two tower blocks were acquired in south London containing self-contained flats, which were upgraded and rented to staff. In Sutton, however, many nurses had homes in the immediate area so that only a relatively small block was provided for nurses working there. A social club, tennis court and swimming pool were provided at Sutton for the benefit of all staff.

Nurses' pay has always been poor compared with other professionals and even in 1904 the matron was given only £80 per annum, although living quarters and all meals were provided. It is interesting to note that just before the NHS was set up a new matron was offered £500 per annum by the Board but the Royal College of Nursing objected, stating that the salary was too high since in their view it should be based on the number of beds. In this case the Hospital contended that their matron carried special responsibility because of its status as a cancer hospital and having large extra out-patient areas to cover, including the rapidly expanding radiotherapy service. A compromise was reached whereby the Board gave a salary of £250, rising to £375 as basic salary but added £100 per year for looking after 'large and special departments'. At about this time nurses' pay was increased throughout the country although the Government only funded 50% of the increase, which may sound familiar to contemporary ears. From 1946 all nursing salaries depended on national policy and agreements over which the Hospital had no control.

In the early 1900s the nurses were judged on a rating scale from very good to bad on the following characteristics:

obedience;	punctuality;	observation;
conscientiousness;	kindness to patients;	method;
trustworthiness;	industry;	bedmaking;
temper;	cleanliness;	personal neatness; and
general conduct.		

Nothing about education, intelligence or knowledge here, but some nurses were determined to change all this for the better.

Modern nursing methods and training in the Hospital began about 1961 when a post-registration course in cancer care was started with a part-time sister tutor. Previously there had been general training in association with Guy's Hospital and later with Portsmouth, but in truth the Hospital needed fully registered nurses for its specialist treatments rather than student nurses.

The first sister tutor was Pamela Newbury who had 12 interested students, including three from overseas, and while a previous attempt at nurse training in cancer care had failed in 1958, this one succeeded. The course lasted for six months and consisted of four study weeks as well as clinical placements around the Hospital. Most of the lectures were given by medical staff, with tutorials by ward sisters. Miss (later Dame) Kathleen Raven, the Chief Nursing Officer at the Ministry of Health, gave advice on setting up the course and also suggested that the sister tutor take tuition at the Institute of Effective Speech. When Miss Haythornthwaite, the matron, retired in 1964 and Pamela Newbury took on the role at the London branch she brought new energy to the nursing area. In that year the special terminal care ward which she had, with others, promoted and planned was opened. Here nurses could learn about the special needs of cancer patients and their families when the disease reached its final stage. It was a successful venture and soon a similar ward was opened in Sutton. At first these wards (Horder and Chevalier) were run by trained nurses but no single doctor was in charge of the special needs of the patients. This need for a medical specialist was resisted

Figure 9.1 Participants in the first post-registration course on cancer nursing. The matron (Miss Haythornthwaite) and the course tutor (Pamela Newbury) are seated in the centre row on the right

and denied by some consultants but later the hospital did appoint a senior lecturer, and then an NHS consultant to run the ward. Thus an excellent palliative care service was given within a cancer hospital – perhaps the first of its kind in Europe. Further innovation followed when the Board agreed in January 1965 to open visiting on all wards, one of the earliest hospitals in the UK to do so. Pam Newbury (later Boulton) resigned and her post was taken by a man for the first time. Graham Joyson was only 30 and full of new ideas. He introduced the specialist nurse concept to the Hospital, starting with a stoma care nurse, and he appointed another young man, Robert Tiffany as director of Nursing Studies. There were two matrons then but when the post in Sutton was vacated in 1973 Joyson became Principal Nursing Officer, responsible for the whole hospital. He was keen on the training courses, having been the first gold medallist himself, and they were

Figure 9.2 Mr Robert Tiffany OBE standing outside the front door of the Royal Marsden Hospital in London

expanded to include study days and short courses. He resigned in 1976 to take up a very attractive post in Australia and was replaced by Robert Tiffany.

Board papers reveal that although the heads of nursing had been present at their meetings since 1961 they said little and their reports were generally bland and made no special contribution to discussions. This all changed when Mr Tiffany took over. His reports never failed to include some mention of the successes, great and small, of his staff, and of the educational expansion he was orchestrating. For example, in 1976 he commented that more than 2000 nurses, students and visitors had visited the Royal Marsden. Nursing could no longer be taken for granted. Furthermore, he announced that he proposed to appoint new specialist nurses in breast cancer care and a community liaison nurse councillor for the palliative care ward. There was already a stoma care nurse and nurses began to take over the venesection work previously done by laboratory technicians. This activity soon extended to administering cytotoxic drugs and setting up intravenous infusions.

At that time intravenous cancer treatment was becoming more fashionable and more complex, so considerable time was taken to draw up the appropriate doses and in doing the venous cannulations. Doctors were glad to pass this on to skilled nurses but the RCN was less enthusiastic, feeling that any ensuing mistakes must remain the responsibility of the doctor even if he had nothing to do with the procedure. This was accepted by the medical staff, which says much for their confidence in their nurse colleagues. The result was a faster, more efficient and very effective service. Each team nurse had practical and other training: lectures were given about available equipment and its appropriate use, as well as on the efficacy, pharmacology and toxicity of the drugs to be administered. There was immediate benefit in terms of a dramatic reduction in local reactions (down to 0.2% for extravasation of fluid) and the number of failed cannulations. The intravenous team is now a common hospital feature but in the mid-1970s it was very unusual.

Other opportunities for specialist nurses occurred as each multidisciplinary unit was developed, including gynaecology, paediatric oncology, head and neck tumours and acute leukaemia, the last having special emphasis on bone marrow transplantation.

Alongside the drive for specialization Bob Tiffany expanded and improved the nursing courses so much so that the RMH was the first to gain approval from the Joint Board of Clinical Nursing Studies for its cancer nursing courses. The first approved course for registered nurses began in October 1974 and that for enrolled nurses one year later. With a pattern of three intakes of registered and two of enrolled nurses annually, the Hospital became the largest provider of cancer nurse training in the country. In the 1980s it was estimated that between 80 and 90% of qualified cancer nurses in the UK were provided by the school. In 1985 there were 500 applicants for 120 places on the courses. By the early 1990s 10 courses had been approved by the Joint Board. As a natural consequence Tiffany and his staff sought, and obtained in 1988, a partnership with the University of Manchester for a BSc degree programme for 10 nurses who completed the course through part-time study at the RCN. Then an MSc course in Advanced Clinical Practice (Cancer Nursing) was agreed with the University of Surrey starting in 1989. Six of the RMH specialist nurses gained the degree in 1995.

In May 1990 the department was rewarded by the foundation of an Academic Nursing Unit headed by Dr Jessica Corner as the first senior lecturer. The post was funded by Cancer Relief Macmillan Fund. In 1996 Dr Corner was appointed to the first Chair in Cancer Nursing in Europe. By this time M Phil and PhD degrees were open to nurses through supervised research and Bob Tiffany's dream had been realized. Although he did not live long enough to see the Chair formally granted it seems he knew it was bound to happen.

There were other initiatives pioneered by nurses, including the production of patient information booklets. The first, a pamphlet on radiotherapy, appeared in 1978. Now there are more than 30, each dealing with treatment and its consequences, as well as information about the disease and where to get help both within and outside the Royal Marsden Hospital. A nursing research unit was formed in 1984 to conduct nursing research separate from medicine, although many nurses were also actively involved in collaborative work with medical staff.

In 1984 the nurses published a *Manual of Clinical Nursing Policies and Procedures* for the speciality, which has been widely used in other hospitals.

The final area of innovation arose out of a review of rehabilitation services which Tiffany and others thought needed reorganization. The review confirmed his concerns and resulted in concentration of all the services involved being rehoused in an old building which had previously contained a laundry, a hostel-type ward and junior doctors' accommodation. The plan was supported financially by the Board, the Marie Curie Foundation and the King Edward's Fund. The unit was opened in 1988 just three years after the review. It housed physiotherapy, occupational therapy, psychological and spiritual support, a lymphoedema and speech therapist as well as a dietician, community liaison, breast care and stoma care nurses in one block. The group was lead by a single person whose job it was to co-ordinate these services and to encourage a holistic joint planned approach to the rehabilitation of each patient. It has been a great success both for staff and their 'clients'. A similar concentration of effort is planned for Sutton.

Bob Tiffany was a special person with many talents. During his long stay at the Royal Marsden (1967–1993) he raised the profile of nurses so that they became truly the equals of other health professionals. The standard of nursing care and teaching within the Hospital became the envy of many and the joy of the patients who experienced it. Bob had an international reputation and was President of the International Society of Nurses in Cancer from 1984–1992. He instituted and then organized their first and second meetings in London in 1978 and 1980. He was also a council member of numerous national and international bodies on cancer nursing. His unique contribution was recognized by the Distinguished Merit Award of the European Society, by the granting of the Fellowship of the Royal College of Nursing and when he received the Order of the British Empire. Despite all this Bob Tiffany remained an approachable and fun-loving human being who never forgot his primary commitment to patient care.

While the success of nursing at the hospital owes much to Bob Tiffany, I am sure he would agree that his vision was realized by his excellent and loyal staff.

Chapter 10

INFORMATION TECHNOLOGY

One of William Marsden's passions was collecting numerical data on the activities of his hospital and from the beginning the Cancer Hospital recorded the number of patients coming to its dispensary, and later to the Fulham Road hospital. The number of new patients, their sex, age and the site of the cancer was noted, as well as the probable outcome of treatment. Thus the Annual Report of 1853 states that a total of 650 patients had been seen at the dispensary since it opened in 1851, of whom 125 were men and 525 were women. The number of women coming to the Hospital has always been greater than men, mainly because of the preponderance of breast cancer in the general population and a mass in the breast was easily diagnosed as a tumour, where internal cancers were referred more commonly to general hospitals. Out of a total of 726 women seen by 1854, 432 were said to have breast cancer. Further, it was noted that the number 'improved after treatment' was 98, of whom only eight had surgery. In recording the site of the tumour there seems to have been a certain prudery in the terminology used for some body areas. One was called 'the generative organs' of which there were 16 male cases and 66 female ones. An attempt at staging the disease was made by a crude description of the tumour as hard or scirrhus, soft or medullary, surface or epithelial and, rarely, osteoid or colloid. The surgical staff felt that this classification was unhelpful and later adopted a system which described the extent of tumours as 'local tumour, ulcerated tumour, and widespread tumour', a remarkably modern approach. Two hundred and thirty-six of the 650 early cases were in the ulcerated stage. By 1894 tumours were classified by their histological features as well reflecting the growing interest and recognition of the importance of the microscopic diagnosis of various tumour types. Even in these early reports it can be seen that while a handful of children and young adults were coming to the Hospital the average age of the patients was 43, at a time when it was said that the average age at death for Londoners was only 27. Indeed, as early as 1856 the surgeons were seeking correlations between cancer and the environment and they noted that there was no association between poverty or poor sanitation and the incidence of cancer.

By 1871 the Annual Report included the Registrar General's figures on deaths, which showed an apparent increase in cancer. The number of deaths attributable to malignancy was 8,800 in 1868 and 9,500 in 1870. The increase caused some alarm to the surgeons. However it may well be that the increase was due to a rapidly enlarging population and improved diagnosis. For some years records of where the patients came from were kept and even in 1885 it was evident that patients were being referred from all over the country, with occasional cases from overseas. Naturally most lived in London or the home counties and this pattern has continued to the present day.

In 1903 a new method of recording medical data was introduced with a view to making analyses of clinical material more effective. As a result reports were prepared on cancer of the mouth and tongue, which suggested an apparent association of cancer in these areas and 'some forms of cardiovascular disease when they were preceded by gout or by syphilis'!

The 1914–1918 war changed many things and the Annual Reports and gathering Hospital statistics lapsed and were not reinstated in the same form again. From then until the early 1940s little change or development of information or statistical recording seems to have taken place. A junior medical post, called Registrar, lapsed. He had been the principle recorder of clinical data and since most of the surgical staff visited on a part-time basis little interest was evinced by them for research in the Hospital – they considered this was the responsibility of the newly formed Research Institute.

The radiological and pathological departments, however, did keep records of the number of investigations performed and the number of radiotherapy treatments (rather crudely measured) with X-rays and radium. In 1942 the radiotherapy department brought in a punch-card system using Hollerith cards and a mechanical sorting machine which allowed correlations to be made using large numbers of cases relatively rapidly. Unfortunately it was not taken up by the rest of the Hospital and the punching of individual cards with a large number of items was very time consuming so was often left to the lay clerical staff to do as best they could. The data was also punched retrospectively, which meant that accuracy depended on all the information being recorded by doctors on appropriate occasions, an ideal which was rarely achieved. The lack of consistent data in patient records has defeated many information systems – even modern ones. It is only when a check-list of questions has to be answered, as in clinical trials, that all cases have appropriate data recorded, and unfortunately doctors have been the most undisciplined of all health professionals in this regard.

Despite all the problems the punch-card system worked quite well and, combined with a very efficient follow up of all patients which had been instituted in 1939, it was innovative and useful.

Efforts to improve data collection were made in a number of departments but the medical committee did not show much interest, nor did the Institute. The clinical group of the ICR was mainly concerned with clinical trials of new agents against cancer and needed details of all patients to be readily available for analysis. Thus Dr Galton, the head of the department, began a system of charting the progress of all patients on graph paper. At first only blood counts were recorded, but it soon became

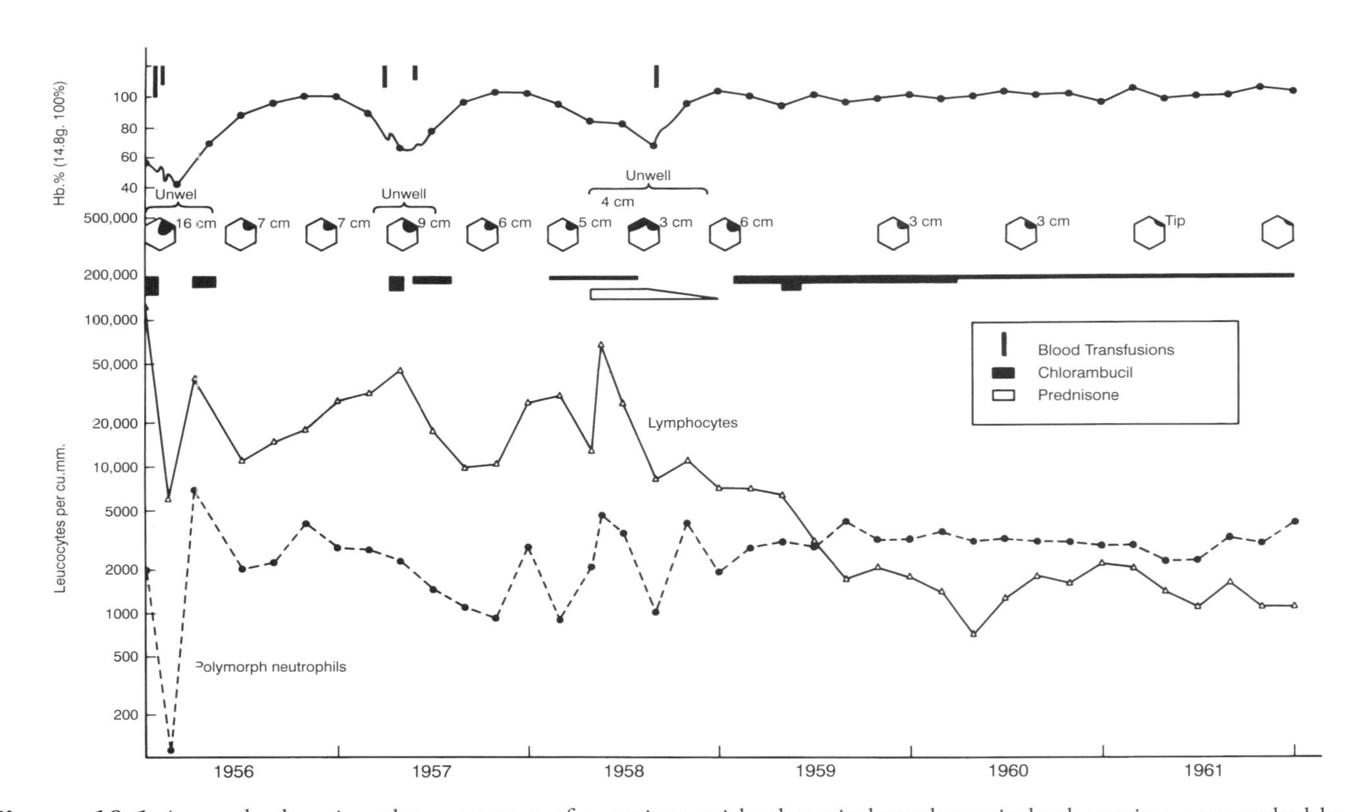

Figure 10.1 A graph showing the progress of a patient with chronic lymphocytic leukaemia as recorded by the chemotherapy group of the Institute of Cancer Research

clear that white cell and platelet counts rose and fell exponentially with treatment, and that other useful data could be recorded on the graph and associated directly with the date and with other information. The graph was semilogarithmic to show the rapidity of change in the white cell counts and treatment was included as well as weight, renal or liver function tests, even the size of measurable tumour masses. Predictions could be made on the behaviour of the blood counts on single patients and consistent data could be analysed retrospectively on any number of patients. While the method was immensely popular with visitors from abroad it was not taken up by the other departments within the Hospital. Within the medical department graphs remained in use until computerisation took the hard work out of the system.

In the early 1960s a lecture on computer technology was given in the ICR. At the end of the lecture Alex Haddow, the Director made the comment that while a computer could not tell you whether a correlation was relevant or stupid it would never make the kind of errors humans are prone to. The example he used was the old chestnut trick question by showing a slide on which was written 'Paris in the the spring'. After questioning, many of the well-educated audience had read 'Paris in the spring'. In 1965 a conference at the Royal College of Physicians on the use of computers in medicine created a lot of interest but there was no support from the Department of Health and little was done about computing in the NHS for many more years.

As elsewhere, computers in the Royal Marsden were first used to perform calculations rather than store and retrieve data. The driving force behind this was Roy Bentley of the joint RMH/ICR physics department, who in 1966 arranged for a data link to be installed to the Atlas computer at London University. This link was little more than a paper tape punch and reader connected to a telephone line and all the results had to be printed by feeding the paper tape output from the data link into a very slow printer. In spite of being so cumbersome the data link was used extensively for dosimetry calculations in radiotherapy, and the benefits of this were so clear that Roy Bentley was able to obtain a research grant for a small computer dedicated to the task of radiotherapy treatment planning, which was installed at the beginning of 1969. Although the PDP8 stood 6ft high and cost the equivalent of about £100,000 it was the forerunner of today's personal computer, with a screen which displayed dose distribution inside body outlines and a plotter to produce hard copy. Roy Bentley was joined by Jo Milan when the PDP8 was installed and together they produced a software package for radiotherapy treatment

Figure 10.2 Jo Milan, the major architect of the present computer system at the Royal Marsden Hospital

planning which was called RAD8. This remained in routine use at the Hospital for 15 years and was eventually used by more than 100 cancer centres throughout the world.

Apart from radiotherapy, Roy Bentley's main interest was diagnostic imaging and he did much of the early work with enhancing images of isotopic scans. But the application of computers to imaging really came of age when EMI developed the computed tomography (CT) scanner in the mid 1970s. The Royal Marsden Hospital was one of the first in the world to obtain a CT scanner as a result of the good offices of an ever generous public in response to a specific appeal. The scanner was of particular importance to a cancer centre because of its potential for better tumour location. The success of RAD8 made this hospital a natural partner for EMI to develop systems to link CT images to radiotherapy treatment planning, an endeavour much helped by the expertise of Anne Cattell, the head of therapeutic radiography, and Roy Parker of the physics department. Since then the Royal Marsden has become a major centre for research in CT imaging, mainly due to the pioneering work of Professor Janet Husband.

During the 1970s the need arose for computer systems to store and process data, particularly to support clinical research. In 1977 the first central computer was installed in Sutton to enable patient data to be accessed from many different terminals around the Hospital. The machine was funded by the Institute of Cancer Research in collaboration with the RMH, with the objective of capturing data automatically in the process of providing operational support to various hospital departments. For example blood test results were captured on the system in the haematology laboratory and could then be communicated directly from the laboratory to the wards or out-patient clinic, and stored for later use. The machine was the PDP11, which was 14ft long and 6ft high with only 64 kilobytes of memory and was served by 16 terminals. The computer cost the equivalent of £550,000 and needed two staff to run the system. For comparison it is interesting to note that a modern personal computer has about 1000 times as much memory. Two back up discs were also bought, costing £20,000 each for 100 megabytes of memory, whereas today ten times the computer memory can be bought for just £150.

By 1979 Jo Milan was devoting all his time to the hospital computer system, and in parallel with the development of operational systems referred to above, facilities were incorporated to maintain and analyse the data required to study specific types of tumour. A pilot study was set up in support of a breast cancer clinical trial being run by Dr Trevor Powles in Sutton. His staff, with support of out-patient and specialist nurses, fed in clinical data from paper records on all cases. The data were consistent and could then be related to blood count results which were fed in automatically, as were some other test results. Over the years these facilities have been greatly extended and now cover all aspects of patient investigation and care. Moreover they have supported a large number of different studies involving more than 40,000 patients. The author well remembers a conversation she had with Jo Milan when he first put forward his plans for 'describing the Hospital in computer terms'. It all seemed like an impossible dream then. His concept meant that a hospital must be described by what it did for and around a patient, thus every activity must be related to the patient and related to the date of that activity. He recognized that retrospective data was full of inaccuracies and that where possible data should be given to the computer directly from source. The learning curve for departmental staff was long and hard, so it took several years before all areas of data were covered but slowly the culture changed and more paperwork was abandoned.

Many useful lessons had been learned with the pilot study but the computer staff came under increasing criticism since the investment was large and to begin with the benefits seemed small. Everyone wanted to have their data computerised and because many small programs could be bought cheaply some departments wanted to buy their own systems for local use. Milan resisted this approach because the data generated would be isolated from the main system he was building. Later his approach was completely vindicated.

Year by year more departments were incorporated, but it soon became clear that the major costs were incurred by areas which were necessary to support general hospital services but contributed little to research. Recognizing the value of the service component, in 1981 the Hospital took over running the central system with the responsibility for staffing and future capital costs. At that time the computer department had five staff and the system used around 20 terminals. By 1994 the staff had grown to 30 and there were 700 terminals, while personal computers are connected to the central system. These developments coincided with the introduction of new management arrangements in the NHS and later with a system of charging purchasers for services, entailing additional requirements to associate cost with activity, so new information was added to the computer database, including administration, payroll, finance and staffing.

Partly because the computerization of the Hospital was designed to integrate research data with patient management data, and partly because of progressive systems modernization, the Royal Marsden has been able to produce one of the very few truly integrated hospital information systems in the UK. The use of a single common database for all applications has meant that all patients' data can be accessed as a coherent record and these data can be translated directly into treatment costs for business management purposes. Most recently the clinical narrative of patient case notes was brought on line so that the Marsden is now poised to be one of the first UK hospitals to replace paper case notes with a fully electronic patient record. This considerable achievement has been possible because of the long-term support of the Board and the dedication of the staff, but unfortunately there was no help, financial or otherwise, from the Department of Health.

Chapter 11

MANAGEMENT AND HOSPITAL BENEFACTORS

It is extraordinary to recall that before the NHS was set up many hospitals were entirely funded by charitable donations, and the RMH was no exception. Its foundation rested on the will of one man, William Marsden, who with the help of his friends and very quickly with wider support from wealthy and less wealthy individuals, was able to develop the Cancer Hospital from a clinic working in rented accommodation to a free-standing wholly-owned hospital for both in-patients and out-patients.

Benefactors usually subscribed annually, while others gave single donations, although a few gave large contributions. One of the earliest windfalls came from a Mrs Wilson of Eaton Square, who gave £4500, a very large sum in 1854 and for which a ward was later named after her. A ward was also named after a Mrs Wolrige who left £5000 to the hospital in her will. Shortly afterwards the patronage of Miss Burdett-Coutts was won. Her interest was very important for apart from her great wealth she also had many influential friends, including the Duke of Wellington and Charles Dickens.

Angela Burdett-Coutts was the granddaughter of Tom Coutts, the banker. He married twice: first to Susan Starkie a 'servant', and second to Harriet Mellon, an actress. All three of his children were girls: Fanny married the Marquis of Bute; Susan married Lord Guildford; and Sophie married Sir Francis Burdett. Angela was the youngest daughter of Sir Francis and

Sophie Burdett, and was born in 1814. When Tom Coutts died he left everything to his wife Harriet, who passed the fortune to Angela who was then still a young woman. Miss Coutts had a lavish life-style but was immensely rich, with an estimated annual income of £80,000. However, over her lifetime she spent large sums on good causes, some of which received as much as £200,000. Her philanthropic interests included the poor, the church, Ireland, and hospitals. In 1857 she loaned the Cancer Hospital £4000 to buy the freehold of a site in Fulham Road enabling the present London branch to be built there. Furthermore she continued to support the hospital for at least the next 20 years with annual subscriptions and other donations. It is uncertain whether the hospital ever repaid the loan and she is remembered there by her named ward and by the portrait of her which hangs over the main staircase.

Angela Burdett-Coutts must have been an unusual character and perhaps took after her grandfather, since she also scandalized her circle by marrying for the first time at the age of 67 a 27-year-old man. The union seems to have been a success. Miss Coutts was the first woman to be honoured with a Baronetcy in her own right in recognition of her philanthropic work, and when she died she was buried in Westminster Abbey.

In 1860 Queen Victoria changed from general hostility about the value of a cancer hospital to supporting it with an annual subscription and a gift of a brace of pheasants. Since then the Crown has honoured the Cancer Hospital with its patronage, including the Duke of Connaught, son of Queen Victoria, King George VI and now Queen Elizabeth II. Most recently Diana, Princess of Wales showed more than a passing interest in the Hospital and its work. She made her first solo official engagement to the Hospital in 1982, and continued to visit often, both officially and privately, until her tragic death in 1997. In 1989 she agreed to be President of the Hospital and to lead the appeal to raise £25 million from the public for the redevelopment of the London site and the building of a modern children's unit at Sutton. Even when her charitable interests were

Figure 11.1 Diana, Princess of Wales with two patients at the opening of their new children's unit in Sutton in 1992

much reduced after her divorce the Royal Marsden continued to benefit from her commitment. Her last efforts in this regard were to open an international breast cancer symposium in Chicago in June 1996 and to attend the previews in London and New York in connection with the auction of her dresses for

Figure 11.2 The parents and children entertain the Princess of Wales in their new unit (1992)

charity. In both cases the RMH would have benefited, together with other charities of the Princess's choosing. When she died on 31 August 1997 the Chief Executive of the Marsden, Miss Cunningham, who knew her well wrote: 'Her genuine concern for the plight of others, her warmth, compassion and the gift of making everyone feel so special were a reflection of her true self and we all feel her loss very deeply at the Royal Marsden.'

Several other large donors from the early years must be included here. They are Sir George Meeson and Sir Massey Lopes, both members of the hospital board. Meeson gave £20,000 towards the building of the chapel and his generosity is commemorated in a stained glass window there, while Lopes bought all the chapel fittings and gave £2,000 for ward fittings. All these contributions and others helped in building extensions to the hospital in 1883 and were crucial to its survival into the 20th century.

Among all the generous gifts were also some rather strange ones, such as one from a Mrs Hall of Brockly, who in 1884 gave 'pictures, men's underclothes, cards and three old pieces of mackintosh'!. Others gave books, cast off linen, newspapers, magazines, flowers and fruit.

After 1900 when expenses rose rapidly because of the introduction of X-ray and radium into medical practice single donors bought radium and installed the first electric lift, both anonymously. *The Daily News* installed a radio service for patients in 1925. However the next major benefactor was Alfred Chester Beatty, who joined the Board in 1937 and was later made vice-president during the presidency of Lord Granard. Chester Beatty, later knighted, was an industrialist who was born in Canada but later made his main residence in Ireland. He took a considerable and practical interest in the Hospital and especially in its research work. The Hospital Research Institute provided on the campus in 1907 was proving inadequate to house all its activities and Chester Beatty came to the rescue with an offer to buy the freehold of the nearby Free Masons Hospital on Fulham Road and to equip it fully. At the same time he equipped the radiotherapy department with more radium and a 200kv X-ray machine. Naturally the Hospital was delighted, and between them Chester Beatty and Lord Granard made the institution ready for the rapid advances in cancer treatment and research which were to follow shortly thereafter. The research building is now named after Chester Beatty and is part of the larger Institute of Cancer Research. Lord Granard and Sir Alfred Chester Beatty were both presidents of the Hospital.

Between the end of the second world war and the introduction of the NHS all hospitals came under increasing pressure to get more money from the public. This was partly because of the increasing costs of medical care and research and also perhaps because high personal taxation reduced the amounts available from the individual donors. Advertisements for funds were a constant feature in daily newspapers and the Cancer Hospital also put in appeals. Sometimes the appeals were endorsed by famous men, even Winston Churchill advertised in support and wrote:

> The Royal Cancer Hospital is doing work of which the nation should be proud. It is fighting this fell disease – trying to establish its cause and discover a cure – providing beds for patients and keeping those who are inoperable free from pain. If those who have contemplated, even for an instant, the possibility of being one day themselves in the clutch of cancer, subscribe to the fund, the present difficulty of raising sufficient money to continue the work, should be easily overcome.
>
> (*The Times* 27 February 1946)

When the NHS was set up hospitals were not allowed to appeal to the public for funds, although they could accept freely given donations. But in 1974 at the instigation and with the support of a Mr Bunzl, a good friend to the Hospital, its own Cancer Fund was set up under the chairmanship of Lord Cadogan. It was used to buy specific expensive items which were not financed by government. This was the mechanism employed for the latest large appeal to which Diana, Princess of Wales, gave so much of her time. The £25 million raised included some individual gifts of £1 million or more from Gary Weston of United Biscuits, the Clore Foundation and the Wollfson Foundation. In addition the Government contributed about £10 million. The total took about three years to collect mainly due to the great efforts of the President, the Chairman (Marmaduke Hussey) and the Chief Executive.

One group which has been most helpful to the Hospital for almost all its existence started as the Committee of Ladies in 1858. It was formed with a view to visiting and helping patients. Its annual report of 1859 states that: 'This has been done to the great satisfaction of the patients.' In 1935 it became the Ladies' Association. Its aims included supporting the work of the Hospital, – both research and patient amenities. Its activities encompassed the care of the garden, providing Christmas gifts for patients and equipping new wards. It also raised money from its members and the public, and in its

Figure 11.3 The original Hospital garden in London

first 18 months gathered £1,303 while 10 years on its annual income had risen to about £6,000. During the 1939–45 war the association opened and ran a canteen for patients and staff, all with volunteer effort. Responsibility for the canteen was taken over by the Hospital in 1944 after the death of a Mrs Elizabeth Robertson, a member of the Association and the prime contributor to the canteen's success over several years. Tragically she was killed in an air-raid in July 1944. At this point the Association opened a free canteen for out-patients. The canteen continues to this day, although it is no longer entirely free. The Ladies had a mobile shop and library for patients, and more recently a permanent shop manned again by volunteers. They continued to help the hospital after the NHS took over. They restarted Christmas parties which they had run for out-patients before the war and in 1951 100 people attended. A hairdressing salon was opened and a garden behind the Hospital was redesigned and replanted. When the Sutton site was opened their activities were duplicated fully on that site.

In the 1960s the Association paid for the building and equipping of the chapel at Sutton, at a cost of £15,000. In 1967 the name was changed again to League of Friends of the Royal Marsden Hospital in order to widen its appeal to the general public, and a Junior League was formed which runs an annual charity ball. The League has been so successful that in 1992 it was able to fully equip one of the new operating theatres at Fulham Road, requiring a commitment of £200,000.

While a district general hospital may continue to function and to serve its local population despite poor management, the same cannot be said for a specialist cancer institution, which must attract its patients from a wide area. The Royal Marsden has been fortunate in this regard for most of its existence. To begin with the Hospital was really the private fiefdom of one man, William Marsden, supported by a committee of laymen and with the help of a secretary. After Marsden's death his son Alexander and the reigning group of surgeons took most of the management decisions and Mr Hughes, a faithful secretary, enabled the Hospital to fulfil their wishes, though he seems to have taken no part in decision making. Mr Hughes died in harness in 1885 after 13 years' service. When his post was advertised there were 300 applicants. It is said that one secretary had a fatal flaw, namely gambling. Apparently he was seen one afternoon in his office, on his knees, praying that his chosen horse would win. Unfortunately for him it did not and he had backed it with the entire salaries and wages of the hospital. He was dismissed but there is no record of a prosecution. Mr Pinkham was a much-loved secretary, who retired in 1943 after many years of devoted service, recognized when a ward in Sutton was named after him. Secretaries, later designated House Governors, were enablers for the Board of Governors rather than initiators of change, and it was often the loudest medical voices which got the support and resources rather than the most deserving. However, hospital buildings and infrastructure were always well maintained and constantly improved due to the efforts of the House Governor.

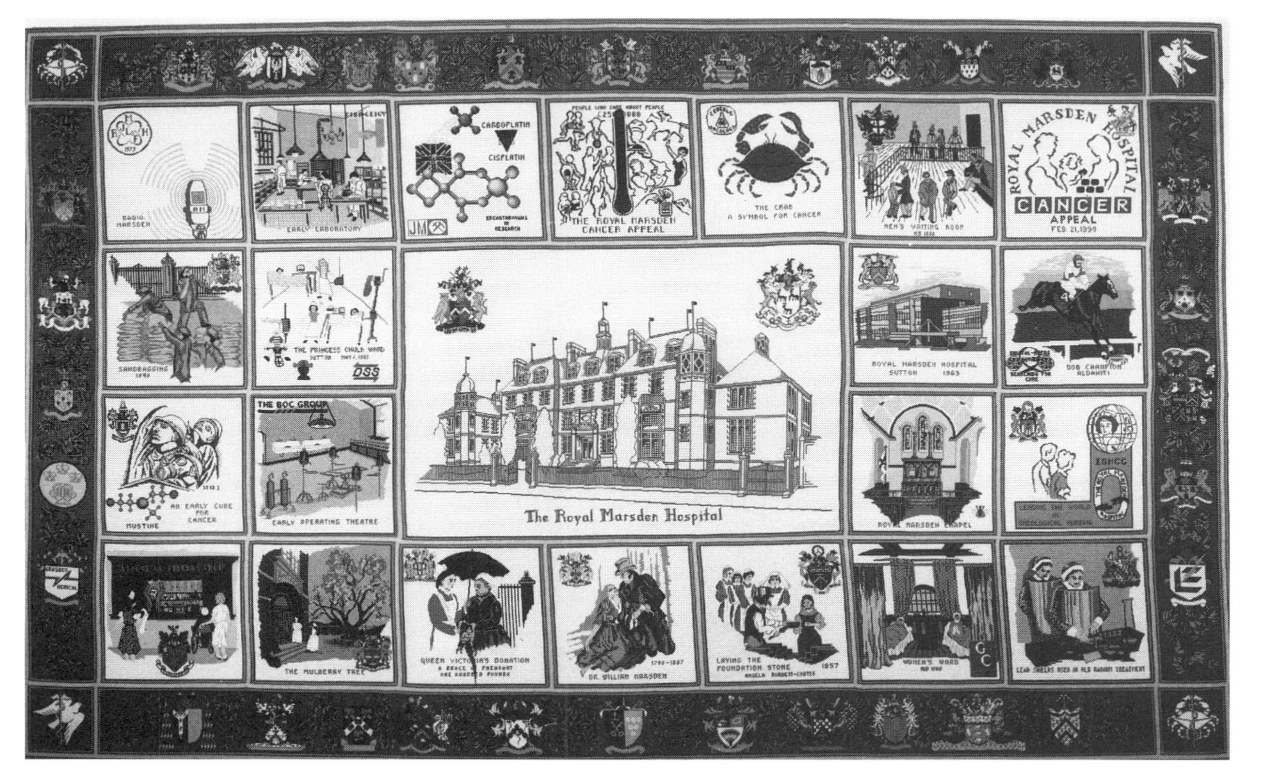

Figure 11.4 A large tapestry produced by the League of Friends recording some landmarks in the history of the Hospital and Institute made in support of the Hospital appeal in 1989

In 1987 the Government introduced new powers together with more responsibility for management. The House Governor post became in turn General Manager then Chief Executive. Phyllis Cunningham was appointed, having been House Governor since 1980. Now the position had much greater power for change and Miss Cunningham took on the challenge. She saw the need for radical changes in the way the Institution was run and major upgrading of the buildings,

Figure 11.5 Miss Phyllis Cunningham CBE, Chief Executive of the Hospital until 1998

especially in London. She slimmed down the management structure and appointed a Director of Clinical Services from within the medical staff. There were also other medical management appointments, but elected representation was abolished. Some of the changes were not entirely welcome to medical staff but she had the support of the Board and in particular the Chairman, Marmaduke Hussey. Together these two set about raising the money for new buildings in London and Sutton which lead to the successful appeal for £25 million. Phyllis Cunningham was honoured for her entrepreneurial work when she won the Business Woman of the Year Award in 1991. The award is sponsored by Veuve Cliquot champagne, and is usually given to business executives with successful companies, indeed this was the first time the award had gone

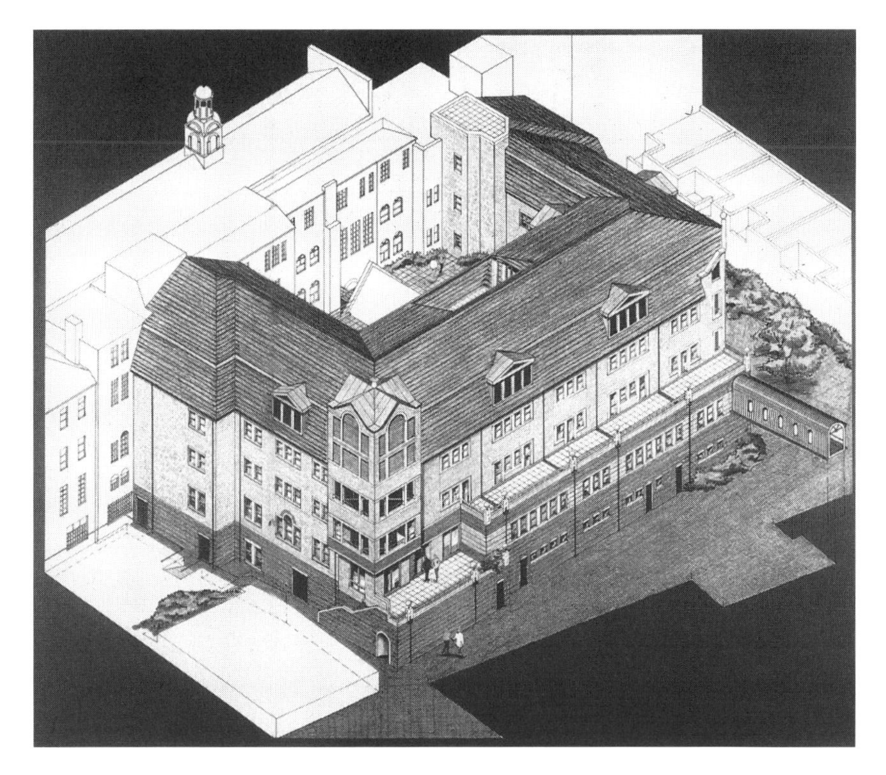

Figure 11.6 Drawing showing the new wing to the London site mainly financed by public generosity in 1992

to a public service manager. It is considered the most prestigious award for a woman in business. Her value to the Hospital was further confirmed when the Conservative government granted the Royal Marsden Hospital a Charter Mark Award in 1995 for excellent service to the public. Undoubtedly Phyllis would insist that both awards were due more to the work of others, but the lead came from her.

INDEX

Numbers appearing in **bold** refer to figures.